Popular Gemology

Oriental Figure Carved in Siberian Aquamarine
[From Ward's Natural Science Establishment.]

Popular Gemology

Richard M. Pearl

DEPARTMENT OF GEOLOGY
COLORADO COLLEGE

REVISED EDITION

Science Editions®
John Wiley & Sons, Inc.
New York · London · Sydney

Dedicated with affection

to my wife's mother,

Mignon Preston Wardell

First Science Editions Printing 1965
Printed as a Science Editions Printing by permission of Richard M. Pearl
Science Editions Trademark Reg. U. S. Pat. Off.

PRINTED IN THE UNITED STATES OF AMERICA

Preface

This book is intended to present in popular language for the general reader the most recent accurate knowledge about the world of gems. It was planned to fulfill the need for a semi-technical survey of modern gemology—simplified, authoritative, and up-to-date. It is written for the gem lover, the mineral collector, the jeweler, and the lapidary.

Completed since the war, *Popular Gemology* is timed to include the new scientific and industrial uses of gems, both natural and artificial, as well as the most recent developments in commerce brought about by the war, and current locality and production information.

A systematic arrangement of subject matter has been attempted throughout. The chapters describing the individual gems have been divided primarily according to the major style of cutting (facet or cabochon) which is generally most appropriate for each gem; the cutting in turn depends upon the inherent characteristics of the gem and so fits into a logical yet original grouping.

Within the chapters the order of gems, with only a few unavoidable exceptions, follows the best scientific classification of minerals, that given in the seventh edition of *Dana's System of Mineralogy*,[1] two of the five volumes

---

[1] Palache, Berman, and Frondel, Harvard University. Published by John Wiley and Sons, Inc., New York. Volumes I–III, 1944–1962.

of which are unpublished. This sequence is surely superior to a meaningless alphabetic listing or the usual arrangement by value, which is always subject to personal interpretation. Diamond, by fortunate coincidence, occupies the first position in either a commercial or a scientific succession. Emphasis has been placed consistently on the mineral family, series, and species as the natural units. Careful attention has been devoted to nomenclature, in order that no technical word should be employed in a wrong sense to simplify its use.

Popular Gemology was conceived in Oregon, begun in Tulsa, Oklahoma, continued in Denver, Colorado, and Cambridge, Massachusetts, and completed in Colorado Springs. It was undertaken at the suggestion of Dr. Henry C. Dake of Portland, editor of *The Mineralogist*, who was to have been co-author but was obliged to withdraw under the pressure of business. In addition to the idea, Dr. Dake contributed the title, the chief basis of classification according to type of cutting, and many of the photographs. For all this assistance and encouragement I am deeply in his debt. Acknowledgment should also be made to the other individuals, educational institutions, and industrial firms that furnished photographs; their names are printed at the proper places in the book. My personal thanks go to Professor Edna D. Romig of the University of Colorado for assistance in a number of the more subtle points of composition; and to my wife, Mignon, for her continued cooperation in every phase of the work, ranging from typing to the actual invention of several of the important parts of the book.

RICHARD M. PEARL

COLORADO COLLEGE
Colorado Springs

Contents

CHAPTER

Chapter 1

The Lure of Gems

The fascination which gems have always held for men and women goes beyond the shadowy dawn of antiquity to the very beginnings of the human race. Its origin must lie in stages of development even antedating mankind; for a bird will pick up bits of brightly colored twigs and twine in preference to more somber ones with which to build its nest, as we choose objects to ornament our clothing or our person.

Whether gems as personal adornment preceded or were subsequent to gems as amulets and charms is debatable. It was easy for primitive peoples to ascribe supernatural powers to especially attractive or otherwise unusual stones that they found in the beds of streams, on the slopes of hills, and on the rocky floors of the hospitable caves where they sought shelter from inclement weather or unfriendly animals. Whichever came first, ornament or talisman, the benefits of both were soon combined in the same piece.

The evolution of jewelry forms parallels the progress of the lapidary art. Earliest of all articles of jewelry was probably the necklace. At first, rough pebbles were

1

merely drilled and strung, but refined techniques led by steps to the rounding and then to the polishing of the natural shapes, although crystal faces were often carefully preserved. From the stringing of necklaces to the making of bracelets was a close transition, since beads were used for both. The introduction of the gem-set metal bracelet and the invention of the ring awaited a more advanced culture.

Amulets whose purpose as such is undeniable were produced from gems and common stones by marking them with prayers and images. The inhabitants of Babylonia, Assyria, and Persia carved such inscriptions and figures into long beads called *cylinders*, which were pierced lengthwise for wearing. These were also used as seals. At about the time of the 9th dynasty in Egypt the *scarab* became prominent in art; this is a representation of a beetle, symbol of the immortality of the soul, and was employed for both seals and amulets.

Not least among the achievements of Greek and Roman artists was their gem engraving. Exquisite craftsmanship was encouraged by the high value and small size of the material at their disposal. The superior durability of most gemstones has made possible their remarkable preservation through succeeding centuries, so that even today we see the gems essentially as they appeared to the original owner. Furthermore, a pageant of classic art in miniature is revealed, showing accurately its struggle for recognition, its Golden Age, and its eventual decadence.

As the variety of designs expanded and the treatment became more personalized and naturalistic, the number of gems regularly used increased. A notable improvement was the introduction of the *cameo* about 300 B.C., the design being carved in relief for decorative purposes only, in contrast to the older form called the *intaglio*, in which the design was incised into the surface of the gem to serve most faithfully as a signet in those not-too-literate days.

After the classic era, the art of gem engraving declined, to be revived with new spirit in the Renaissance and again, with far less originality, in the 18th century. Present-day gem carving, though still done with hand tools, is on a more commercial basis.

A love of gems characterizes all races and all social levels. There have been few famous persons in history who have not been traditionally identified with a particular gem. Private and public collections have been diligently assembled. In Rome wealthy families competed with one another in acquiring choice gems and displaying them in the temples.

The medical or therapeutic use of gems is as varied as the gems themselves. Any disease of man or beast was believed to be preventable or curable by swallowing the powder of the proper gems, chosen for their color or chemical ingredients, or by applying them whole. Strong and no doubt often fatal potions were prescribed on any occasion. Some of these superstitions linger to the present time; necklaces of amber, for instance, are still bought in American stores as a remedy for goiter.

The symbolism of gems ranges from the charming to the bizarre and to the merely ridiculous. As the mystical and religious attributes of gems are compared, it becomes evident that at one time or another almost all the virtues have been ascribed to almost every gem. Formerly, the study of gems was dominated by this aspect of the subject, but the growth of modern science has dispelled much

3

of the ignorance, if not the entire fantasy, surrounding gems, and gem lore has largely yielded to gemology. What were once exclusively trade secrets, guarded jealously and handed down from father to son, have now become the possession of every person who cares to read and learn.

The gemological movement began in Europe. The Gemmological Association of Great Britain was established in London in 1908 as an adjunct of the National Association of Goldsmiths of Great Britain and Ireland. Patterned after it but now greatly expanded in scope is the Gemological Institute of America, founded in Los Angeles in 1931 by Robert M. Shipley; it conducts courses, principally for members of the jewelry industry. An affiliated organization is the American Gem Society, the activities of which are directed toward the education of the trade and the protection of the public; the title *Certified Gemologist* is its highest award. Similar associations are being started in other countries, the newest ones being national groups in Belgium and France.

BIRTHSTONES

The pleasant custom of wearing a special gem that belongs to the month in which one was born seems to have had its origin in Germany or Poland during the 16th century. The arrangement probably corresponded at first to the signs of the zodiac rather than to the calendar months. This idea can be traced back to the twelve foundation stones of the holy city, New Jerusalem, described in the 21st chapter of the Book of *Revelation* or the *Apocalypse*.

Each of the stones was inscribed with the name of an apostle. The direct predecessor of the New Testament list was a different series, consisting of the twelve gems (each engraved with the name of one of the tribes of Israel) which adorned the breastplate of judgment worn by the high priest and described in *Exodus* 28.

The names of all these gems are not always identical in the several lists that appear in the Bible and other writings; discrepancies may be accounted for by changes in the actual breastplate, difficulties in manuscript translation, errors in copying, and inability to identify certain stones by their descriptions. Different races and nations have had their favorite birthstones; a composite selection, partly traditional and partly arbitrary, constitutes the list of natal gems conventionally sold in the United States. Alternate selections of gems have been recommended according to the apostles, guardian angels, zodiacal signs, days of the week, hours of the day, and assorted ideas without end; all of them serve the purpose of supplying a reason for buying a gem which the purchaser usually wants to buy anyway and for wearing a gem which the owner is perfectly willing to wear without apology. We may prefer to believe with Emerson that "Beauty is its own excuse for being"—and a gem for being worn.

Chapter 2

Recognizing Gems

The art and science of gemology deals with certain natural substances and their man-made substitutes, which human beings regard as attractive enough to serve primarily for personal adornment and secondarily for decoration of their possessions. A gem becomes a jewel when it is placed in a setting appropriate to its use.

THE NATURE OF GEMS

Most gems are *minerals*. A mineral is defined as a homogeneous substance produced by inorganic processes, and occurring in nature with a specific chemical composition; it usually has a definite internal structure which may be expressed in typical outward forms called crystals.

A substance is homogeneous when it is uniform even under a microscope; this requirement excludes rocks, some of which appear to be the same throughout but are found upon close examination to be aggregates of several different materials. Products of animal or vegetable life are barred because they are not inorganic. Manufactured chemicals are not embraced among the minerals because they do not occur in nature. The chemical composition of a mineral must be represented by a formula or else be variable according to a dependable law. A definite internal structure implies a three-dimensional pattern of atoms (as shown

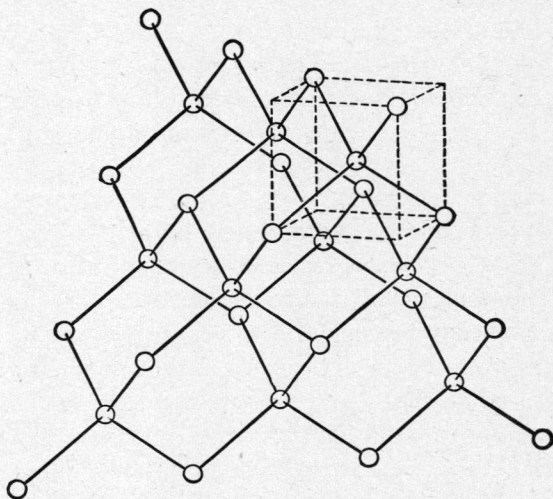

Fig. 1 Atomic Structure of Diamond
[From Dana-Ford *A Textbook of Mineralogy,* copyright 1932.]

in Fig. 1), the arrangement of which is intimately related to the crystal form and to other essential characters.

About 80 of the 1,000 or more mineral species have been regarded as gems, though many of these are met with only occasionally. Diamond, the noblest of gems, is perhaps the most remarkable of all minerals.

A few gems are *rocks.* Members of the so-called mineral kingdom that fail to satisfy the fairly strict requirements of a mineral are termed rocks. Basically, a rock is any mass that forms an important part of the earth. It may be a single mineral such as salt, or a single nonmineral such as coal, or an aggregate of several or more minerals such as granite, or a uniform substance such as volcanic glass, which could be considered a mineral if the chemical composition did not vary so irregularly from place to place. The most highly prized blue gem of ancient times, lapis lazuli, is a rock consisting of at least half a dozen individual minerals. Three gems—obsidian, silica-glass, and tektite—are natural glasses of volcanic origin, having wide ranges in their content of silica.

Although it contains some mineral substance, pearl, "queen of gems," is the product of a living organism. Coral consists of the skeleton of certain sea animals which belong to the same group as the sea anemone. Jet is a plant material, a variety of coal, and so is not properly a mineral. Amber is surely a gem, and one of the loveliest, but it is the fossil resin of ancient trees. These four are *organic gems*.

The synthetics and imitations, that is, the *artificial gems*, do not fit into any of these classifications. They may be regarded neither as minerals, nor rocks, nor organic things, but as chemical creations of the laboratory. Gemology is the only subject which properly considers them from every angle.

Characteristics of Gems

A gem combines three significant qualities: chief among them is *beauty*, so that it delights the eye; then *durability*, so that its beauty will last "unto the third and fourth generation"; and *rarity*, so that one's neighbors may not easily own any like it. Also, of course, a gem must be portable, but, if it is used for personal wear, that can be taken for granted. Lacking any of these qualities, a material may not enter the exclusive ranks of gemology unless it possesses the others to a high degree.

Once a substance is admitted to be a gem, its current value is determined by a combination of economic, commercial, and political factors, such as adequate supply, fashion, publicity and demand, cost of cutting and merchandising, world prosperity and depression, international markets and tariffs. The final price of a very fine gem depends upon the conscience of the dealer and the acumen of the buyer. As the beauty-loving public becomes increasingly aware of the many previously little-known but valuable kinds of gems, the differentiation between *precious* and *semiprecious* stones becomes obsolete. If not commercially, at least aesthetically, they are equal.

Gem Families

As we glance over the rings in a jeweler's show case, we are amazed at the wide variety of gems he displays. But the gemologist would recognize most of them as belonging to a quite limited number of separate species, these in turn being represented by many varieties based mainly on differences of color.

We may liken a gem species to a human family, for example, the Smiths, and compare a gem variety to any individual member of the family. Thus George Smith may be blond, whereas his brother Fred Smith may be dark; yet they belong to the same family. George, however, may look surprisingly like Henry Jones but not be related to him. Again, other men may be named Smith, but if they belong to a different race they are not brothers

9

of George and Fred. A scientific knowledge of gems enables us to trace any stone to its proper place on the gemological family tree.

Gem Properties

To be able to recognize gems requires both a familiarity with their appearance and a knowledge of their nature and characteristics. These qualities are called properties, as coldness is a property of ice, sweetness is a property of sugar, and heaviness is a property of lead. Each known property serves to identify a particular gem or to eliminate other gems as possibilities. At the beginning of the process of testing an unknown gem, all gems and their substitutes of similar appearance are under suspicion, but determining any definite property reduces immediately the long list of gems to a few likely ones. Knowing the properties of gems and being able to find them listed and described in convenient books and tables make gem identification a matter of systematic procedure.

Some properties, such as color, are easily discerned, but others must be weighed and measured, sometimes with elaborate and expensive instruments. Many crystals, as well as a few other specimens, disclose their identity by means of the original forms in which they occur; other gems are most easily recognized by the properties that are revealed after cutting.

Any gem species differs from all the rest in composition and structure. Its chemical elements, their kind and arrangement, give the gem its properties, and these in turn furnish us with the means of identifying the gem.

10

Chemical tests are of little value in the recognition of gems; the information gained is hardly worth the damage done. Resistant as most gems are to normal wear, they still deserve to be handled with reasonable caution, and therefore a chemical examination is not made of cut gems, but only of rough stones or fragments. A few useful exceptions are described later.

The chemical composition itself, nevertheless, is of great importance, if not in the actual identification of a gem, at least for an understanding of its constitution. Most gems are minerals, and the fundamental fact about a mineral is that it is a naturally occurring chemical element or compound. The principal basis for classifying minerals, either scientifically or industrially, is a chemical one.

The colors of gems are due mostly to the presence of chemicals, usually oxides of certain metals, which are often scattered through the stone as minute impurities in such small amounts that they are not included in the chemical formula. (There are only a few self-colored gems.) Such minor constituents make a gem less perfect but at the same time add to its beauty and so increase its price. They probably create more value than anything else in the world of the same weight. For example, each ounce of the chromium that gives emerald its green color adds perhaps a million dollars to the cost of the gem—up to a certain limit, of course, for there is the law of diminishing returns, as well as a saturation point after which too much coloring matter may actually decrease the beauty of the gem. Evidence of the existence of these coloring substances is not revealed chemically, however, but optically, by means of

11

the characteristic absorption spectra described later in this chapter.

Diamond is the simplest in composition of all the gems, the only one consisting entirely of a single *element*, crystallized carbon. Tourmaline, at the opposite extreme, has such a complex formula that John Ruskin said, "The chemistry of it is more like a medieval doctor's prescription than the making of a respectable mineral." Next to diamond in simplicity among the more important gems are the *oxides*, including quartz (an oxide of silicon) and corundum (an oxide of aluminum).

More gems belong to the *silicates* than to the other chemical classes; included among them are feldspar, jade, tourmaline, beryl, olivine, garnet, zircon, and topaz. Turquoise is a *phosphate*. Spinel and chrysoberyl are *multiple oxides* or *aluminates*. Pyrite is a *sulfide*. Fluorite is a *halide*, more accurately a *fluoride*. Smithsonite is a *carbonate*. Of the organic gems, pearl and coral are also largely carbonates, whereas amber and jet are *hydrocarbons*. Oxygen is the chief element present in gems, and silicon, aluminum, and calcium are next in abundance.

The resistance of most gems to chemical action is important from the standpoint of their durability. They may be properly expected to retain their pristine beauty almost forever. The enormously high temperature required to cause even the slightest blackening of a gem diamond is an example of this stability. Glass imitations, on the contrary, become dull even if not worn, because of the deleterious effect of the hydrogen sulfide (which is also the cause of silver tarnish) present in the air.

A few genuine gems are likewise not impervious to ordinary chemical action, and special care should be taken

12

of them. Pearls, for instance, lose their luster if allowed to remain long in contact with body perspiration. The popular belief that the beauty of pearls improves with wear seems hardly justified. The famous story of Cleopatra dissolving two choice pearls in vinegar and drinking them to impress Antony with her wealth is probably not true, because the calcium carbonate is too much associated with organic matter to dissolve rapidly in such a weak acid as vinegar. But the moral is evident to wearers of gems, although it ought to be unnecessary to advise them to refrain from spilling acids on their jewels. All the varieties of garnet are somewhat susceptible to the effects of acid. Hydrochloric acid will attack certain gems, including turquoise, pearl, lapis lazuli, and coral. Two strong acids are the ingredients of aqua regia, which is used for testing gold, and the jeweler should be careful where he places the gems when repairing or cleaning jewelry containing them. Grease may prove progressively injurious to gems that are to any degree porous, such as turquoise, moonstone, and pearl. Caustic alkalies injure emerald, and oil of turpentine removes the red coloring of coral.

Tests, of course, can be made of gems by means of any known property. For obvious reasons, as explained, a chemical examination is rarely made. But with appropriate care a few simple tests may on occasion be worth while.

Ornaments and jewelry of "Mexican jade" virtually flooded the American market in 1943 and are still abundant. The identity of this material with the common mineral calcite is shown by the effervescence that occurs when a drop of hydrochloric acid is placed on it.

On turquoise—advisedly on the under side if the specimen has been cut—a touch of hydrochloric acid leaves a dull spot which turns bright blue when a drop of ammonia is added, thus distinguishing the gem from its usual substitutes. Recent imitations are hard to test, however.

Coral and the other carbonate gems effervesce briskly in acid. Lapis lazuli in acid gives off the rotten-egg odor of hydrogen sulfide. Amber can be distinguished from other natural resins by its refusal to become sticky or dull when touched by a drop of ether.

Just as a variety of a gem may, through gradual changes in the kind and amount of coloring matter, grade imperceptibly into a different variety—as ruby wanes in depth until it becomes pink sapphire—so also a mineral species by variation in its actual chemical formula may grade into a related species, which yet maintains (and indeed must have) the same type of crystalline structure. Thus, the six garnet species are more or less interchangeable in composition among themselves. Other gem minerals, including corundum, spinel, olivine, and topaz grade into nongem species. Both aspects of this relationship are known as *isomorphism*.

Another and more complete type of chemical alteration entirely changes the composition and physical properties of a substance but preserves its characteristic outer form. The transformation is called *pseudomorphism*. Petrified wood is the most familiar example of a gem pseudomorph, the chalcedony variety of quartz having replaced the original substance, wood. As the trees decayed, tiny particles of silica that had infiltrated among the original cells settled out of solution and slowly replaced the fiber.

14

A different condition, called *polymorphism*, exists when the same chemical element or compound produces different minerals. Thus, diamond and graphite are both composed solely of carbon; and three gems—kyanite, andalusite, and sillimanite—share a single formula.

Abbé Haüy referred to crystals as "the flowers of the minerals." It is easy to agree with him, upon examining the beautiful crystals of gems with their symmetrical forms and shining faces. The shape in which we find them is the shape that they have always had, for like people and animals, the larger crystals are merely small ones "grown up." Growth is usually a long, slow process, taking perhaps thousands or even millions of years, although sometimes it may be rapid enough to be seen happening. Crystals vary in size from those that are colloidal and are visible only with an ultramicroscope to those that weigh a number of tons. Unlike living organisms, crystals grow by accumulation from the outside rather than by expansion from within. When growth is interrupted for some reason and then begins again, a "phantom" crystal may appear enclosed within the larger one.

Crystal structure is a fundamental property of minerals and crystal shape provides a valuable clue to the identity of a rough specimen. Crystallography is largely mathematical in treatment, and in part it is very complicated. An elementary knowledge of crystals, however, is worth having, if only for the ability that it gives to name many gems in their native state without testing them further.

15

The regular external shape of a mineral is the outward evidence of its internal atomic structure. If a crystal is broken or cut for jewelry, each piece, no matter what its size or outline, will still have the same internal pattern, as shown by X-ray studies. All gem minerals, with the possible exception of opal, are *crystalline* substances, as are also those artificial gems that are correctly called synthetics. The minute particles, the atoms and ions, of which they are composed, are arranged throughout in a definite, orderly manner and are held together in a "lattice" by electrical attraction, usually that of oppositely charged electrified units called ions. *Amorphous* or *noncrystalline* substances were created under conditions unfavorable to a systematic arrangement of their atoms, which are arranged instead mostly at random. The difference is somewhat like that between soldiers at inspection and a group of children watching a fire. Amorphous gems may be fashioned into any neat design, but their internal structure is still irregular and they can never be crystalline. That is why the term "rock crystal" for even the finest of etched glassware is wrong; only natural unfused quartz should be thus designated.

The "habit" of a gem crystal is the form or combination of faces typical of it. Sketches and models show an ideal shape, but in nature crystals are never perfect, some being malformed, others broken—just as every tree is bent a little, every flower is a bit distorted, and every person has some blemish which distinguishes him or her from the figures in the tooth-paste advertisements. Nevertheless, the angles between the natural faces are always constant and are more accurate than human skill could make them. In addition to individuals, crystals occur as twins, three of which are illustrated in Figs. 2–4, and in groups.

The large number of crystal forms may be separated into six main divisions called *systems*, according to the arrangement of *axes* within the stone. (See Figs. 5–10.) These axes are entirely imaginary, however, like the poles of the earth or the lines of latitude and longitude on a

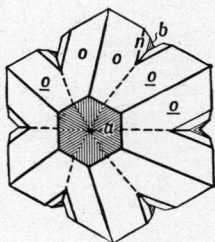

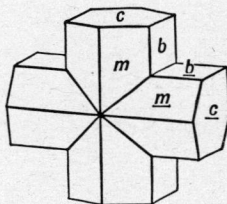

Fig. 2   Fig. 3   Zircon   Fig. 4   Staurolite
Chrysoberyl

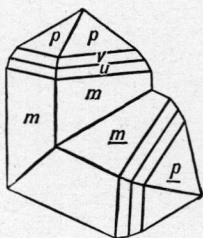

Models of Typical Twin Gem Crystals

The letters are conventional symbols for the common "forms." [From Hurlbut *Dana's Manual of Mineralogy*, copyright 1941.]

map, and like them are extremely useful. The six systems are called isometric, tetragonal, hexagonal, orthorhombic, monoclinic, and triclinic. Each of them has three axes except the hexagonal, which has four. The axes in the isometric system are of equal length. The six systems may further be subdivided into a total of 32 *crystal classes* or 230 *space-groups*, according to *symmetry*. Practically all gems, as well as most minerals, are confined to a relatively few of these categories.

This classification of crystals is not in the least arbitrary or artificial, in spite of the imaginary conception of an axis. The atomic arrangement of minerals determines

17

most of their properties. Since the internal structure determines the crystal forms also, it follows that certain
properties, the optical properties in particular, must be

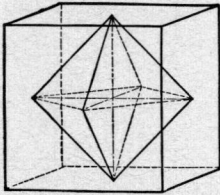

Fig. 5   Isometric   Fig. 6   Fig. 7
                          Tetragonal   Hexagonal

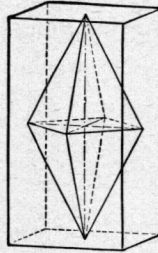

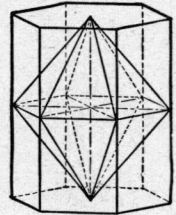

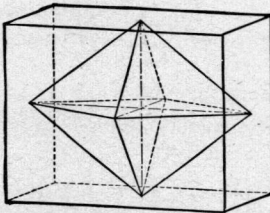

Fig. 8   Orthorhombic   Fig. 9   Monoclinic   Fig. 10
                                                  Triclinic

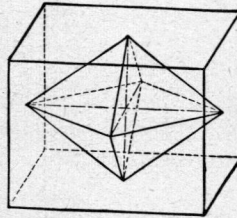

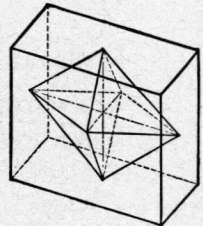

The Six Crystal Systems

Each model shows how different "forms" may have the same crystal
axes. Many other combinations are possible in each system. [From
Dana-Ford *A Textbook of Mineralogy*, copyright 1932.]

related to the crystallization. The identification of a gem
is largely dependent upon a knowledge of the crystal
system to which it belongs. Let us take the systems one
by one and mention some of their characteristics; later we

shall learn how such theoretical considerations of gemology are intimately related to the practical testing of gems.

To gain a better understanding of what crystals are, shake out a few grains of common table salt and look at them with a magnifying glass—pretty little cubes they are! Now it is easy to understand why this system is called the *isometric*, meaning equal measure: all sides are equal and

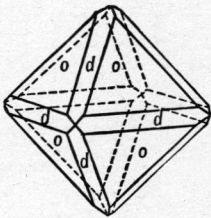 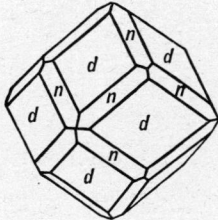 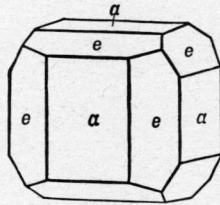

Fig. 11   Spinel   Fig. 12   Garnet   Fig. 13   Pyrite

Typical Isometric Gem Crystals
[From Hurlbut *Dana's Manual of Mineralogy*, copyright 1941.]

the angles between them are equal. These facts are true of all simple members of this system, whether or not the crystals form a cube. Diamond, for instance, usually occurs in octahedrons resembling two square pyramids placed base to base, but the sides and angles do not vary from the requirement. Other isometric gems are spinel (Figs. 11 and 71), garnet (Figs. 12 and 78), fluorite (Fig. 72), sphalerite, and pyrite (Figs. 13 and 81).

The *tetragonal* system is usually represented by prisms and pyramids. The most important gem representative is zircon (Figs. 14 and 79); cassiterite (Fig. 15), scapolite, and idocrase (Fig. 16) are also tetragonal.

19

Some of the finest crystals belong to the *hexagonal* system. It is not generally realized that snow and ice

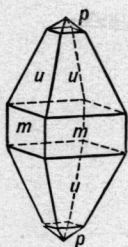

Fig. 14
Zircon

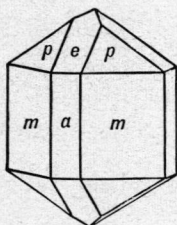

Fig. 15
Cassiterite

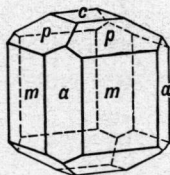

Fig. 16
Idocrase

Typical Tetragonal Gem Crystals
[From Hurlbut *Dana's Manual of Mineralogy*, copyright 1941.]

are minerals, but photographs of snow crystals taken under a microscope show their wonderful six-sided structure.

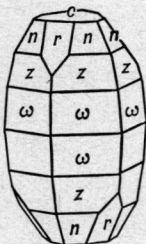

Fig. 17
Corundum

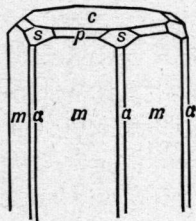

Fig. 18
Beryl

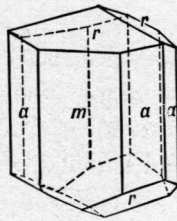

Fig. 19
Tourmaline

Typical Hexagonal Gem Crystals
[From Hurlbut *Dana's Manual of Mineralogy*, copyright 1941.]

Corundum (ruby and sapphire, Figs. 17 and 70), beryl (emerald and aquamarine, Fig. 18), tourmaline (Figs. 19,

20

75, and 76), and quartz (amethyst, rock crystal, etc., Fig. 93) are the best-known members of this system. Quartz crystals occur, both alone and as large clusters, in familiar prisms which are pointed at the ends and are the most easily recognized of all the minerals. Beryl, because of its flat terminations, is also quickly identified. Tourmaline is

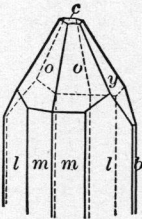 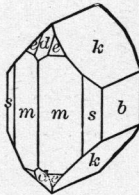 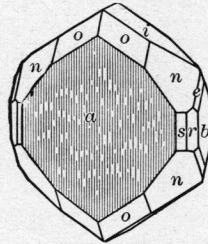

| Fig. 20 | Fig. 21 | Fig. 22 |
| Topaz | Olivine | Chrysoberyl |

Typical Orthorhombic Gem Crystals

[From Dana-Ford *A Textbook of Mineralogy*, copyright 1932.]

the only mineral that shows a triangular outline when viewed down the length of the crystal. Additional hexagonal gem crystals include apatite, benitoite (Fig. 74), phenakite, willemite, and hematite.

Gems that belong to the *orthorhombic* system are often complex in their crystal forms. The most important ones are topaz (Figs. 20 and 80), oiivine (Fig. 21), and chrysoberyl (alexandrite and cat's-eye, Fig. 22); lesser ones include cordierite, danburite, andalusite, sillimanite, and staurolite (Figs. 90–92).

Gem crystals of the *monoclinic* system include spodumene (hiddenite and kunzite, Fig. 73), orthoclase feldspar (moonstone, Fig. 23), and sphene (Fig. 24), as well as

21

brazilianite, diopside, epidote, datolite, euclase, and gypsum (satin spar, Fig. 25).

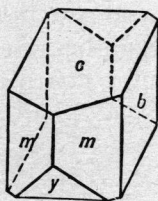
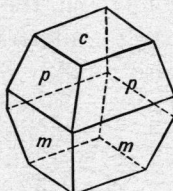

Fig. 23
Orthoclase
Feldspar

Fig. 24
Sphene

Fig. 25
Gypsum

Typical Monoclinic Gem Crystals

[From Hurlbut *Dana's Manual of Mineralogy*, copyright 1941.]

The *triclinic* system is represented by microcline feldspar (amazonstone, Fig. 85) and plagioclase feldspar (lab-

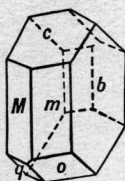
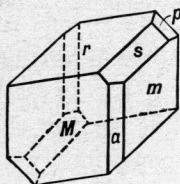
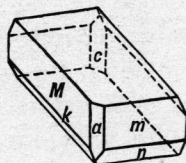

Fig. 26
Plagioclase
Feldspar

Fig. 27
Axinite

Fig. 28
Rhodonite

Typical Triclinic Gem Crystals

[From Hurlbut *Dana's Manual of Mineralogy*, copyright 1941.]

radorite, Fig. 26), axinite (Fig. 27), kyanite, and rhodonite (Fig. 28), and by the only turquoise which has ever been found in crystals.

22

Some gems act as if they were ashamed of themselves and attempt to conceal their identity by assuming the forms of quite different substances. In addition to this type of replacement, described in the previous section as *pseudomorphism*, gems occur also in imitative shapes, for example,

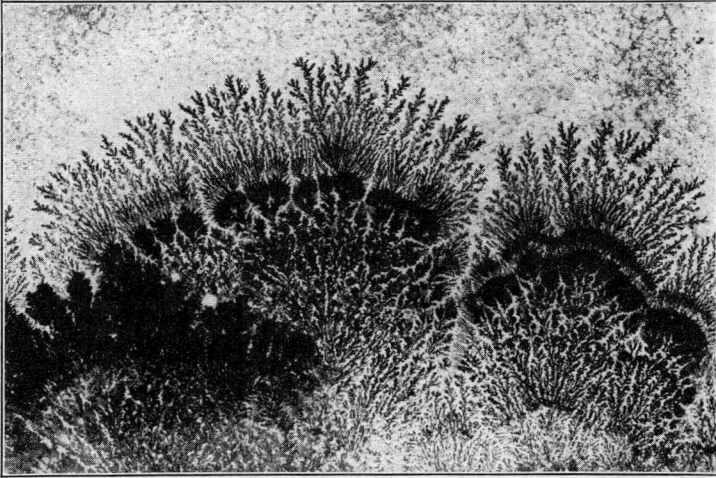

Fig. 29   Dendrites on Marble

when chalcedony resembles a bunch of grapes, and when agate or marble shows manganese or iron markings that look like trees and moss (see Figs. 29 and 95). Gems whose irregular outer shapes do not warrant distinctive names are referred to as *massive*.

In spite of the fact that most of the properties of gems are directly determined by their internal structure, no one has ever seen an atom. Because they are so small, millions of them can occupy an inch of space. But their presence and even their position are subject to proof. In 1912 von

23

Laue passed X-rays through a crystal and onto a photographic plate. The many symmetrical spots that appeared on the plate (see Fig. 30) were found to be visible evidence of the atoms in their specific arrangement. Further re-

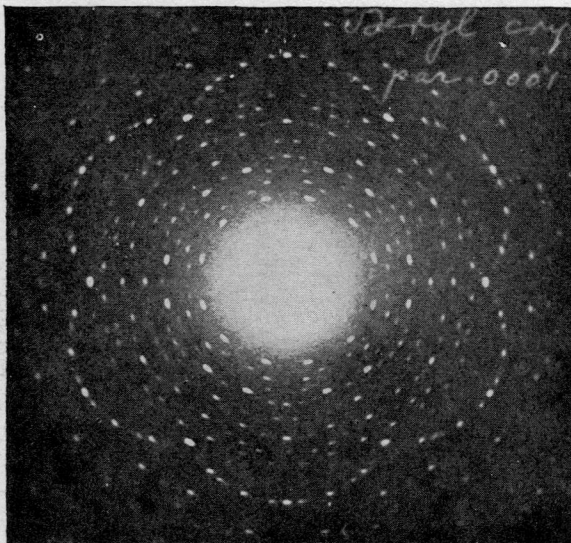

Fig. 30 X-ray Picture of Beryl (Emerald and Aquamarine)
[From St. John and Isenburger *Industrial Radiology*, 2nd edition, copyright 1943.]

search has opened the door to a vast field of knowledge regarding the structure of crystals—those marvelous examples of Nature's architecture.

OPTICAL PROPERTIES OF GEMS

It is the effect of light upon a substance which determines whether it is beautiful, and beauty is the prime attribute of every gem. *Optics*, the science of light, is therefore the most important part of gemology. In ordinary technical usage it is generally considered a branch of physics, and the properties of minerals are hence divided into those that are physical, including optical, and those that are chemical. The great significance of optics in the study of gems, however, as contrasted with the small practical value of chemical tests, such as have already been discussed, justifies a further separation here into optical properties and physical properties.

Color

Through the doorway of color we enter the enchanted world of gems. In former times gems were recognized mainly by their colors, green stones being called emerald and red stones ruby, so that the superstitions which gathered about a gem applied to all of a similar color. The wealth of curious gem lore is concerned mostly with the symbolism of color. The intense emotional effect of color language appears through all literature.

It seems probable that the explanation of the fact that women are more responsive than men to the lure of gems is the physiological one that they have a superior sensitivity to color stimuli. Men are often at least partially color blind, but women are rarely so and generally have a more acute judgment of color.

Without beauty of a degree high enough to please almost everyone, no substance, however rare or durable, can secure entrance to the select circles of gem society. Usually color is the main factor of beauty, and in some instances it is the only factor, as in stones that are not

25

transparent or brilliant, such as coral, jade, lapis lazuli, turquoise, the chalcedonies, and especially opal. Because the permanent beauty of gem colors is, therefore, the chief single reason for the firm hold that precious stones have always had upon the affections and the imagination of mankind, the study of color in gems is one of the gemologist's most important tasks. It is approached from the scientific as well as the aesthetic viewpoint.

Color is, in a sense, all that we see of light. It is mostly a difference in color, no matter how little, that makes an object visible against its surroundings. White light consists of separate rays or wavelengths, successively red, orange, yellow, green, blue, indigo, and violet, all perfectly blended and reaching the eye simultaneously. By means of a simple glass prism, such as Newton is said to have bought at Stourbridge Fair for a penny, his classic experiment may be repeated, and a beam of sunlight may be split up into its sequence of rainbow colors, called the *spectrum* (see Fig. 41).

When white light is reflected from the surface of a stone or passes through it, some of the component wavelengths are absorbed, while the rest unite to produce the color of the gem. (The process of absorption causes a transfer of energy from light into heat, which means into the motion of the atoms of the gem itself.) Slight but uniform absorption results in a colorless stone, whereas complete absorption makes it black. The precise hue of the gem depends upon the extent to which the parts of the spectrum are eventually transmitted to the eye. Anyone listening to orchestral music can easily distinguish the high notes of the violins from the low notes of the horns. But unlike the ear, the eye fails to make such a separation

Fig. 31 Jeweler's Loupe Fig. 32 Utility Magnifier

Fig. 33 Hand Lenses

Magnifying Instruments for Examining Gems

[Bausch and Lomb; American Optical Co.]

and can see only a blending of colors. Red light and green combine as yellow; blue and yellow, being complementary, are seen as white. Actually the color of most gems is such a harmony of hues. Amethyst appears violet because it returns only those rays whose combined frequency—that is, number of vibrations per second—gives the effect of this particular color. The same rule applies to opaque gems.

Yet the vast mystery of color remains largely unsolved. One may even say that we do not know anything about what causes color—what makes one flower yellow and another violet; why one form of chromium colors emerald an exquisite green, and a different form of the same element gives a glorious crimson to ruby. So too it may be said that we do not know what electricity is, but we harness its power and press it into our service. Since Newton observed his first spectrum, color technology has constantly progressed, and chemists have devised artificial sources of coloring materials which have helped to brighten the lives of us all.

Gemology shows how often appearances are deceptive. Many of the stones which look alike have no similarity other than their color; some which seem to have no resemblance whatsoever are really "sisters under their skins." Mere traces of foreign matter, accidentally introduced, may give a wide range of hues. Those stones whose color is caused by chemicals that are an inherent part of them are called *idiochromatic;* if the color is eliminated, the identity of the stone is destroyed. Most gems, however, are *allochromatic;* the color is an incidental characteristic; if it were altered or removed the essential properties of the stone would remain as they were before. It is not easy to visualize the sameness of two gems that look as unlike as a red ruby and a blue sapphire—both varieties of the same mineral, corundum, differing only in color.

Thus color, though surely the most important quality in a gem, may be the least reliable guide to its identification. But the delicate color sense possessed by many persons can distinguish the subtle yet vital differences in hue that characterize most individual gems and are peculiar to them. Even without this precise ability, knowing the approximate color narrows the choice of gems to relatively few. In spite of all sensible advice to the contrary, therefore, most persons will continue to rely on their instinctive judgment of color to make a preliminary guess as to the name of a gem.

Printed descriptions of gem colors are of little use for this purpose, and practical experience in the actual handling of gems is necessary. When this way is no longer effective, because of the difficulty of discriminating between several gems of the same color, aid is sought from one of the instruments (described later) that analyzes color, such as a spectroscope (Fig. 47) or dichroscope (Fig. 48).

Streak

Some gems, like many humans, show their true color when put to a test. The test of a gem is to determine its color when it is finely divided. By rubbing the stone on a piece of unglazed porcelain, such as a rough white tile, a powdered *streak* is made, which may have a color very different from that of the solid specimen.

Many minerals have a characteristic streak, but only a few gems show the property in any color except white.

Of these gems, hematite is the most important. As a metallic dark-gray gem it has been worn for years in a larger number of men's signet rings (carved with intaglio portraits) than all other gems combined. By its rich reddish-brown streak it can be distinguished from any other gray or black mineral or substitute. Pyrite, another iron mineral, appears to have a metallic yellow color resembling brass, but its streak is almost black with a greenish or brownish cast.

Reflection and Luster

When light strikes a gemstone, some of it is reflected immediately from the surface, some of it is absorbed at the surface, and the rest passes through. (See Fig. 34.) The amount that is reflected varies according to the direction of the light and the nature of the gem. Only a small part of the light falling perpendicularly is turned back to the eye, but most of the light is reflected when the angle is small. The greater the reflection, the brighter the stone will appear.

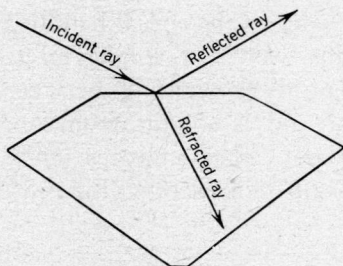

Fig. 34 Reflection and Refraction of Light in a Gem

This appearance of the surface of a gem in reflected light is called *luster*. Hard stones which have a more closely knit surface structure can generally be given a higher degree of polish than others; in consequence they will allow less light to penetrate and more will be re-

30

flected. A rough surface scatters the light and gives a diffused luster, as in stones that are soft (such as turquoise) or have a granular texture (such as certain jade). The common, though hardly sanitary, habit that mineral collectors have of wetting with their tongues a newly found agate to bring out its color serves the purpose (besides cleaning it) of providing a thin but level surface of moisture to reflect the light regularly, similar to the result obtained with much more difficulty by polishing the stone. While being polished, the surface of every gem except diamond is momentarily caused to flow, the liquid spreading evenly over the stone in an extremely fine layer.

Gems with a high refractive (light-bending) power produce the most brilliant luster. *Adamantine* luster, as indicated by its name, is typical of diamond. Most gems have a *vitreous* luster, which is simply the surface appearance of ordinary glass. *Subadamantine* luster applies to a number of intermediate gems, including zircon, sphene, and andradite garnet, the lusters of which exceed that of glass but do not quite attain the splendent beauty of diamond. *Resinous* luster indicates the surface of a resin, of which amber is the only gem representative. An oily surface has a *greasy* luster. Fibrous gems such as satin spar show a *silky* luster. Turquoise has a *waxy* luster. The luster of pearl is obviously *pearly*, as is also that of most crystal cleavage faces. The opaque metallic gems, pyrite and hematite, possess a *metallic* luster. Most of these terms are descriptive enough to be evident after a brief examination of a gem that is characteristic of each. Considered especially with its color, the luster of a gem is frequently a useful guide to the quick recognition of its species.

Refraction

The light that is not reflected or absorbed at the surface of a gem enters the interior, where its subsequent action has a profound effect upon the beauty of the gem and is of great value in revealing the identification. The speed of light in air is well known to be about 186,300 miles a second. When it enters a gem, however, light is slowed down, and this change in velocity deflects its direction, except where it happens to strike exactly perpendicularly. We say that the light has undergone refraction or bending, as shown in Fig. 34. Every South Seas native is familiar with this property of light when he spears a fish in water by aiming, not where the fish appears to be, but where he is sure that it really is. The apparent bending of a stick in water is similar evidence of the refraction of light. The slower the velocity of light in a given gem, the greater is the amount of refraction, as if a slow ray were less determined than a fast one and had more difficulty in keeping to its path. In any event, the light that comes in at an angle is bent nearer to a vertical direction.

The actual amount of deviation is determined mathematically and is expressed as a number called the *refractive index*—for diamond it is 2.42, that is, light goes almost two and one-half times as fast in air as it does in the stone. Gems that have a high refractive index are said to be optically dense; in them the light is bent sharply and its velocity is relatively slow. Light that comes out of a gem, as of course it must to become visible, is also refracted but in the opposite direction (that is, away from the vertical) because it is then entering a substance (air) that is optically less dense than the stone.

32

As the angle of inclination of the light within the gem increases, the light finally reaches a *critical angle* (Fig. 35) when it can no longer be refracted out of the stone and unable to escape is totally reflected so that it stays inside.

When *total internal reflection* takes place at the bottom of a gem, as shown in Fig. 35, leakage of light is prevented and the light, instead of passing out through the lower facets, is returned to the top and refracted out from there, adding to the brilliancy of the stone. Light traveling inside a gem emerges from the stone when it strikes a facet surface at less than the critical angle. Conversely, when it strikes at greater than the critical angle, it is totally reflected, without loss, within the gem.

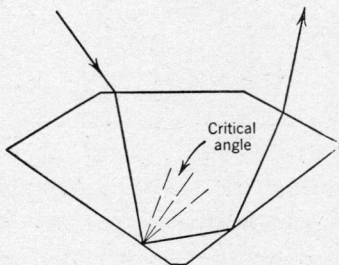

Fig. 35 Total Internal Reflection in a Gem

The critical angle of a gem is inversely proportional to the refractive index. Diamond, for example, having a higher index (2.42) than white topaz (1.61), has a smaller critical angle. (See Figs. 36 and 37.) Less light is lost, therefore, and more can be totally reflected internally in a diamond than in any of the gems that have a smaller refractive index. Skillful cutting enables light to traverse a diamond so as to be returned finally to the eye with as little loss in quantity and as much improvement in quality as possible. Thus the fiery brilliancy is produced that is diamond's chief asset.

A number of methods are available for determining the refractive index. For a cut stone the most convenient is by means of a *refractometer* made especially for gem testing (Fig. 38). This instrument gives a direct reading on a simple scale. The gem is placed with one of its facets

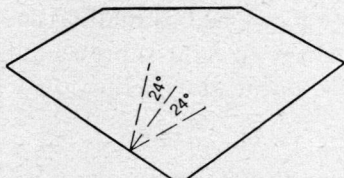

Fig. 36   Diamond   Fig. 37   Topaz

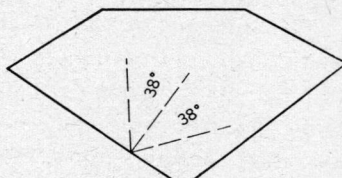

Critical Angle in Two Gems

against the refractometer lens, which is a prism or hemisphere made of glass with a high refractive index; a drop of some highly refractive oil is put between them to ex-

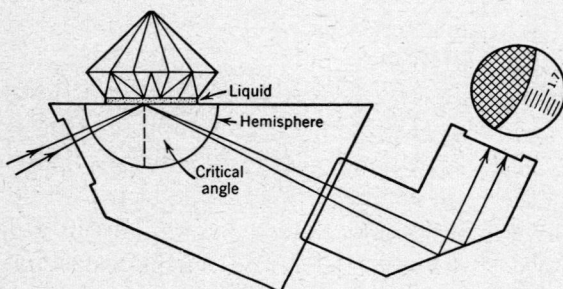

Fig. 38   Section Through a Refractometer

clude the air and bring them into optical contact. Light from an outside source, either natural or artificial, is directed through the refractometer lens and against the flat bottom surface of the stone. The portion of the light that

34

strikes at more than the critical angle is totally reflected, as already described, and produces a band of light, the edge of which is read on a graduated scale (Fig. 39) and corresponds to the refractive index of the gem.

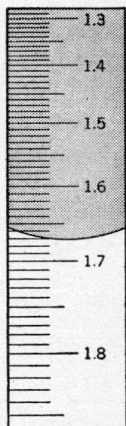

Fig. 39 Singly
Refractive Gem

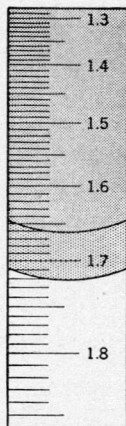

Fig. 40 Doubly
Refractive Gem

Refractometer Scale

The range of standard refractometers is not high enough to include four important gems—diamond, zircon, sphene, and andradite garnet—whose brilliancy is too great and whose critical angle is therefore too small to register, unless a special lens of higher refractive index is used. The very absence of a reading points immediately to one of these four species.

No more fundamental or easily determined property of gems is available for purposes of identification. Typical

35

values, selected from G. F. Herbert Smith's *Gemstones*, are listed here. Two sets of figures are given for doubly refractive gems. (See page 39 and Fig. 40.)

Refractive Index Table

Diamond	2.42	
Sphalerite	2.37	
Cassiterite	2.00	2.09
Sphene	1.88–1.92	1.99–2.05
High zircon	1.92–1.93	1.98–1.99
Andradite garnet	1.89	
Low zircon	1.79–1.84	
Spessartite garnet	1.79–1.81	
Almandite garnet	1.75–1.81	
Corundum	1.76–1.77	1.77–1.78
Chrysoberyl	1.74–1.75	1.75–1.76
Pyrope garnet	1.74–1.75	
Grossularite garnet	1.74–1.75	
Spinel	1.72–1.75	
Olivine	1.64–1.67	1.68–1.71
Spodumene	1.65–1.67	1.67–1.68
Jadeite jade	1.65	1.67
Topaz	1.61–1.63	1.62–1.64
Tourmaline	1.62–1.63	1.63–1.64
Turquoise	1.61	1.65
Nephrite jade	1.60–1.61	1.63–1.64
Beryl	1.56–1.59	1.56–1.60
Quartz	1.54	1.55
Amber	1.54	
Orthoclase feldspar	1.52–1.53	1.53–1.54
Opal	1.44–1.46	
Fluorite	1.43	

Dispersion

The separation of white light into its component colors, accomplished by Newton with his penny prism, proves not only that light is bent upon entering a substance of different refractive index, but also that each color of the spectrum is refracted to a different extent, as shown in

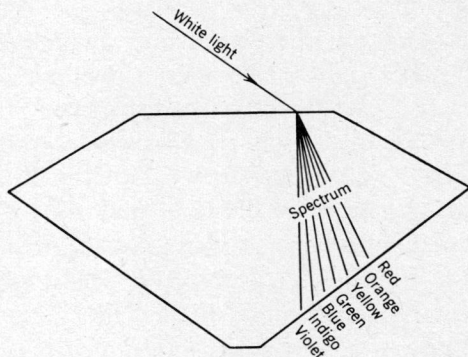

Fig. 41 Dispersion of Light in a Gem
The amount of fire is exaggerated.

Fig. 41. This spread of colors is called *dispersion;* in a gem it is known as *fire.*

A superior example of dispersion is the rainbow; sunlight is refracted and dispersed by countless millions of raindrops which together magnify this simple effect into the wonder of a stormy sky. A myriad of tiny rainbows sparkling in the morning dew, or on a crack in a window, or from the depths of a diamond—these are other familiar dispersion effects.

Red light rays are bent the least, and violet rays at the other extreme are bent the most. Since red rays are bent

37

less than the rest of the colors, their velocity is changed less than that of the others, and their refractive index is slightly lower. Actually, the refractive index of a gem is different for each color, and the difference between the end values of red and violet measures the dispersion. The indices of refraction of diamond, for example, range from 2.41 to 2.45, and therefore the dispersion is 0.04. The wider the spread, the greater is the fire.

Fire is therefore not mere brilliancy, which is internal reflection of white light, although, in general, highly refractive gems also possess the most dispersion. In colored stones the hues of dispersion are masked by the color of the material itself. Contrary to what might be supposed, diamond does not have more fire than any other gem. Both andradite garnet and sphene, as well as cassiterite and sphalerite, surpass it in dispersive power and would appear even more spectacular than diamond if they too were colorless.

Typical values of selected gems are given below.

Dispersion Table

Sphalerite	0.16
Cassiterite	0.07
Andradite garnet	0.06
Sphene	0.05
Diamond, benitoite, zircon	0.04
Epidote, grossularite garnet, spessartite garnet, pyrope garnet	0.03
Almandite garnet, spinel, olivine, corundum, spodumene, tourmaline, chrysoberyl	0.02
Topaz, beryl, quartz, orthoclase feldspar, fluorite	0.01

Double Refraction and Birefringence

The behavior of light as thus far described is strictly true only for gems that are amorphous or belong to the isometric system of crystallization. Gems that belong to the other five crystal systems have a somewhat different effect upon a ray of light. These gems split a single ray

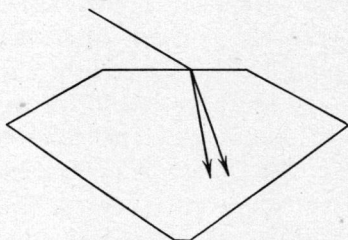

Fig. 42   Double Refraction   Fig. 43   Double Refrac-
in a Gem   tion in Calcite

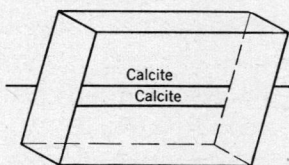

into two new rays, each of which travels with a different velocity inside the stone and is bent a different amount. (See Fig. 42.)   The slower of the two rays is refracted more than the other, and each ray has a separate refractive index, as if the gem had a dual personality.

This double refraction is possessed to such an extreme degree by the common mineral calcite that any mark, such as a line or dot or row of print, shows double when seen through it (Fig. 43).   Although the effect is observed to a much less extent in the gemstones, some gems display it under a magnifying glass, jeweler's loupe, or microscope. A doubling of the edges of the back facets appears when they are viewed through the front of the stone; two lines can be seen for each line that actually joins a pair of facets.

Such an experiment should be attempted only in a state of complete sobriety. The double refraction of zircon and olivine, as well as of benitoite and cassiterite, is so strong that a reading glass is sufficient to show it, and the doubling in sphene can be seen with the naked eye.

A simple test for double refraction, which is perhaps the most satisfactory way to distinguish zircon from diamond, requires only sunshine and a card with a small hole pierced in it. Holding the card between the sun and the stone permits the narrow beam of sunlight that comes through the opening to be doubly refracted by the gem and thrown back onto the card as a group of double spots; it is proved that the gem does not belong to the isometric system and cannot be a diamond.

One precaution is necessary. Gems of the tetragonal and hexagonal systems are *uniaxial* (Fig. 44), having one direction in which the light is not doubly refracted; this direction is called the *optic axis* and must be avoided in making the examination, because it will cause the gem to seem to be amorphous or isometric. Gems of the three remaining crystal systems—orthorhombic, monoclinic, triclinic—are *biaxial* (Fig. 45), having two such directions of single refraction and thus having two optic axes. A gem should, therefore, be inspected in more than two directions before an opinion is expressed.

One of the two rays that form when light enters uniaxial crystals (tetragonal and hexagonal)—it may be either the slower or faster ray, depending upon the gem—varies in speed according to the direction in which it happens to vibrate, and consequently has a variable refractive index, which reaches a certain limit. Biaxial crystals (orthorhombic, monoclinic, and triclinic) also have two rays traveling

40

through them in any given direction, but these gems are much more complex in their optical nature and possess three principal refractive indices.

The amount or strength of double refraction is called *birefringence* and is measured by the difference between the largest and smallest indices, whether there are two or

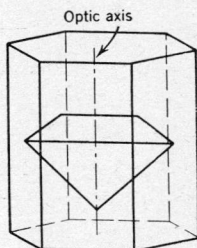

Fig. 44 Uniax- Fig. 45 Biaxial Gem
ial Gem

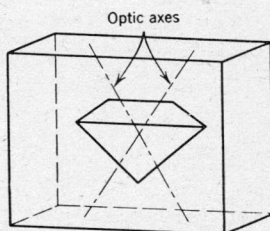

Possible Arrangement of Optic Axes in Gems

three. For example, quartz has two refractive indices of 1.54 and 1.55; the birefringence is the difference, 0.01. Amorphous and isometric gems, being singly refractive, obviously have no birefringence.

When a doubly refractive gem is tested on the refractometer, the band of light ends in two parallel lines. These may move somewhat on the scale as the stone is turned, but their extreme high and low readings correspond to the maximum and the minimum values of refractive index. The most strongly birefringent gems show, of course, the widest separation of the terminal lines.

Typical values of selected transparent gems are given on the following page.

41

Birefringence Table

Sphene	0.12
Cassiterite	0.10
High zircon	0.06
Benitoite	0.05
Datolite, olivine, epidote	0.04
Diopside	0.03
Tourmaline, spodumene	0.02
Chrysoberyl, quartz, corundum, topaz, orthoclase feldspar, beryl	0.01

Absorption Spectra

Light that has undergone dispersion can be analyzed by one of the most amazing tools of modern science, the *spectroscope*. This incredible instrument reveals the particular combination of rays absorbed from the original white light during its passage through a gem. Each ray is a definite part of the spectrum, and those rays that are not absorbed unite to give the color of the gem. A full normal spectrum is seen in a direct-vision spectroscope (Fig. 47) when it is pointed merely at a source of light, but, when a gem is held between them, dark vertical lines or ribbons appear, obscuring certain sections of the spectrum. These *absorption bands* represent the rays that have been removed by the chemicals present as impurities in the gem. Each element produces a characteristic arrangement of bands, which together constitute an *absorption spectrum*. Two gems of apparently the same color may absorb light differently because they are composed of entirely different chemical combinations. Many a gem has its own distinctive absorption spectrum, which, in addition to furnishing valuable knowledge about the cause of color in the gem, is also useful in its identification.

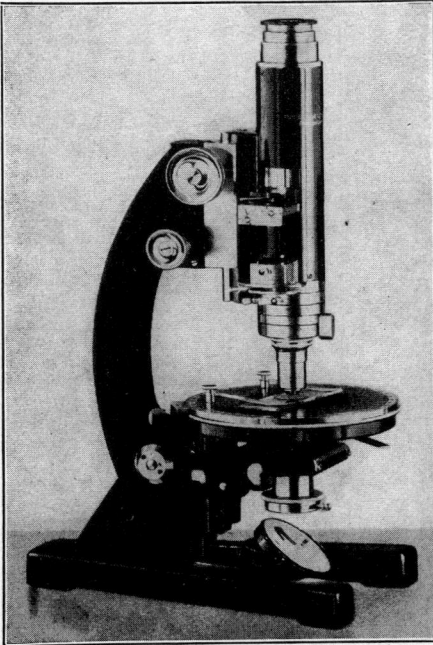

Fig. 46 Petrographic Microscope   Fig. 47 Direct-Vision
                                              Spectroscopes

Optical Instruments for Identifying Gems
[Bausch and Lomb.]

For several important gems the absorption spectrum is particularly useful. Zircon shows through the spectroscope a multitude of sharp bands that conclusively label any specimen. Ruby is rather fickle; its band may be

43

either dark or light, depending upon the source of light, but it is always in the same place. The bands for emerald serve to differentiate it from all substitutes. Almandite garnet was, with zircon, the first gem to be observed with a spectroscope and still is one of the best to be tested in this way. The mystifying change of color seen in alexandrite—"an emerald by day, an amethyst by night"—is explained by its absorption spectrum, which shows a chromium compound having delicately different powers of absorption that vary according to the kind of illumination.

Dichroism

We have already remarked that the color of a gem is in reality a combination of all the hues that are not removed from the original white light in its passage through the gem. Each of the two rays produced by doubly refractive gems not only is refracted differently from the other and acquires a different velocity, but also is usually absorbed to a different extent and has a different color. This twin-color effect is known as dichroism, as the word itself indicates.

The complex biaxial gems (those belonging to the orthorhombic, monoclinic, and triclinic systems) possess three main color directions, corresponding to the three principal refractive indices, but only two colors can be observed at a time.

A few strongly dichroic gems, especially kunzite and tourmaline, may show a change in color as they are turned in various directions. Even weakly dichroic gems are enhanced in beauty by the subtle gleams of color glowing

44

and mingling mysteriously in their depths. To reveal the twin colors of most gems with certainty, however, an inexpensive instrument called a *dichroscope* (Fig. 48) is required. It consists of a short tube having a round opening at one end and a square opening at the opposite end. Between the ends is fitted a piece of the clear variety of calcite known as Iceland spar; a magnifying lens may be added to enlarge the image. Through the round hole the

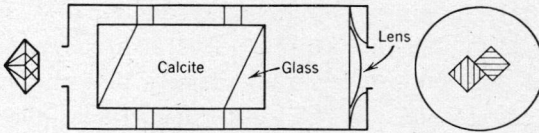

Fig. 48   Section Through a Dichroscope

observer looks at a gem held beyond the square opening. The great doubly refractive power of calcite (Fig. 43) makes this square appear as if it were two squares side by side and intensifies the original double refraction of the gem. Each of the two rays emerging from the gem is seen in a separate frame. Viewing the twin colors next to each other thus simplifies the comparison.

The colors should change places slowly as the dichroscope is rotated, and any difference between them, no matter how slight, is evidence that the gem is doubly refractive and therefore cannot be amorphous or belong to the isometric crystal system. The reverse is not true, however, because not all doubly refractive gems show dichroism. A few, particularly zircons of colors other than blue, are so feebly dichroic that a good imagination is required to see the effect. Obviously, also, since this is a test involv-

45

ing color, no colorless gem can be dichroic. Trying to find dichroism in a colorless stone would be like looking for a white rabbit hiding in a snowdrift. In addition, examination must be made in more than two directions through a gem, because there is no double refraction and consequently no dichroism along an optic axis (Figs. 44 and 45).

This "magic eye" is of the utmost value in gemology, separating many stones whose blending of colors gives them the same superficial appearance. In 1907 some blue stones that looked like sapphires were discovered to be a new kind of gem, and even an entirely new mineral, now called benitoite, because a California jeweler chanced to hold them in front of a dichroscope, which showed him a blue square and a white one, a combination never seen in sapphire.

Among the more important gems, ruby may be unfailingly identified by its distinct twin colors, yellowish red and purplish red, whereas red spinel and garnet (being isometric) and red glass (being amorphous) show no dichroism at all. Similarly, blue sapphire can be told immediately from blue spinel or glass, and emerald can be distinguished easily from demantoid, the green garnet. Precise dichroic effects are difficult to describe, and they vary considerably with the hue of the gem itself, so that a table of dichroism would be useful merely as a hint. The appearance of the colors themselves becomes familiar only with experience. It must be remembered that, except for stray interference from outside light, even the faintest difference between the two colors proves dichroism and double refraction.

Polarization

Polarized light has become a household commodity in America chiefly through the widespread use of sun glasses made from Polaroid Film. This artificial material, composed of synthetic organic crystals embedded in parallel orientation in a plastic sheet, produces cheaply and conveniently the same effects of polarization that occur in minerals. The features of polarized light that pertain to gems have already been discussed under different headings,

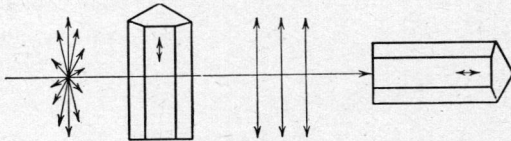

Fig. 49   Light Polarized by a Gem Crystal

but popular interest in this fascinating subject makes it worth while to mention briefly the relationship between polarization and some of the other properties of gems.

Ordinary light vibrates in every direction at right angles to the path in which it is traveling forward, as shown at the left of Fig. 49. These vibration directions may be likened to the spokes of a wagon wheel, although there is no limit to their number; the axle corresponds to the advancing path of the light ray itself. Polarized light, on the other hand, vibrates in only one direction, comparable to a single spoke on each of the opposite sides of the hub, making a straight line at right angles to the moving ray of light. (See Fig. 49.)

Part of ordinary light becomes polarized when it is reflected from the polished surface of a gem, the amount

47

depending upon the angle at which it strikes. Part of the light that enters a singly refractive gem—one that is amorphous or isometric—is also polarized. All the light that enters a doubly refractive gem, however, is completely polarized, except along an optic axis; each of the two rays created by double refraction vibrates almost perpendicularly to the other.

It is this individual restriction of the vibration directions that makes each ray of a doubly refractive gem so distinct in its action and so useful in the identification of gems. When either of the rays is extinguished or obscured, the other predominates. A plate cut from tourmaline absorbs one of the polarized rays and permits only the other to pass through. If two such plates are "crossed," that is, held together, one lengthwise and the other sideways, as shown in Fig. 49, the first plate will pass the light that vibrates in its own lengthwise direction, but the second plate, being set in opposition, will stop the light. This striking phenomenon is shown in Fig. 50. A complete rotation of either plate brings alternating darkness and light four times. A doubly refractive gem rotated between the plates also causes this "extinction" (as the positions of darkness are called) to take place. Singly refractive gems present a dark field in all positions.

A lone plate of tourmaline rotated behind a dichroic gem makes the twin colors alternate. Except that it does not absorb one of the polarized rays, but transmits both of them, calcite acts much like tourmaline. Do you recall now the change in color that occurs four times during rotation of a dichroscope? A section of calcite is called a *nicol prism* when used to polarize light in a microscope. Disks of Polaroid Film (Fig. 50) have the same effect and are a less costly substitute for a natural mineral. A dichroscope is superior for viewing the dichroism of gems, however, because it shows the twin colors simultaneously (Fig. 48), no rotation being necessary to produce a change in color.

Fig. 50   Polaroid Film in Crossed Position

The vibration directions in the two disks are at right angles to each other.   Any light that passes through the first disk is absorbed by the second.   [Polaroid Corp.]

We have seen that both rays of doubly refractive gems are polarized and travel in different directions, vibrating about at right angles to each other.   Each vibration direction has a different color absorption, producing dichroism. From these facts comes the need for the skillful cutting of many gems to yield the best color.   The top facet of

49

a cut ruby should be parallel to the top face of the ruby crystal for the stone to show the richest possible color. Tourmaline, on the contrary, is usually too dark in that orientation, and a more desirable color is obtained by cutting the top facet to correspond to a side face of the crystal.

Unusual Effects

A number of gems are so distinctive in their optical effects that descriptions are entirely inadequate to do them justice. To quote the classified ads, they "must be seen to be appreciated." Once seen, such gems can never be forgotten, and their recognition becomes largely a matter of having a typical specimen.

These unusual phenomena are further discussed, together with an explanation of their cause, in later chapters, under the descriptions of the individual gems.

The reflection of light from enclosed substances arranged in certain crystal directions within a gem gives rise to *asterism*—rays of light extend in starlike fashion across the rounded surface. Star ruby and star sapphire are the best-known examples, though the same property is also seen in some other gems, especially garnet and rose quartz.

A parallel alignment of mineral fibers causes the related condition of *chatoyancy*, which is conspicuously seen as a band of light in such gems as cat's-eye (both the chrysoberyl and quartz varieties), tiger's-eye, and hawk's-eye.

More spectacular even than these are the effects that come from the *interference of light*. The magnificent play of pure color that is the splendor of opal, the vivid

50

sheets of color that sweep across the face of labradorite, and the charming blue sheen of moonstone are alike caused by the conflict of light rays which mingle as they are reflected from thin films and crystal plates within the gem and near its surface.

Luminescence

The amazing effects of ultraviolet light, transforming a mineral cabinet into a fairyland of color, are among the interesting studies of modern gemology. The meaning of luminescence, fluorescence, and phosphorescence—their origin, description, and value in helping to recognize gems—are discussed in Chapter 8.

PHYSICAL PROPERTIES OF GEMS

As explained previously, a consideration of the physical properties of gems may include those that are optical in nature or optical properties may be given separately. The second procedure has been followed in this book, and the purely physical properties that do not deal with light will be presented next.

Weight and Specific Gravity

Gems are usually weighed in *carats*. Before the universal adoption of the metric carat, which was legalized in the United States in 1913, the unit of weight used by gem dealers varied from country to country. A carat was originally the weight of a seed of the carob or locust tree, native to the Mediterranean region. (The word *karat* is

51

quite different and refers to the purity of gold alloy.) The present carat equals one-fifth of a gram, and about 150 carats are equivalent to an ounce. Each carat is divided into 100 parts called *points*, as a dollar is divided into 100 cents. Gems of lesser value may be sold by the gram, pennyweight, or ounce, or occasionally in larger units. Some cut stones are priced according to size, measured in millimeters or inches. Pearls, on the other hand, are sold by the *pearl grain*, four of which are required to make a carat.

Those who handle gems soon recognize that some gems weigh more than others that have apparently the same size. A one-carat diamond is too large to fit in a ring mounting prepared for a one-carat zircon. To express it another way, a diamond and a zircon of the same dimensions have different weights. A zircon simply is heavier than a diamond with the same external measurements; zircon is denser or (as we say) has a greater *specific gravity*, meaning that it weighs more than an equal volume of diamond. This is due mostly to the fact that the elements of which zircon is composed (zirconium, oxygen, and silicon) have greater atomic weights than the single element (carbon) in diamond.

Complicated measurements or special equipment would be necessary to determine the volume of a gem, but when all gems are compared in density with water, the actual procedure for the determination of specific gravity becomes a fairly easy matter. Because most gems are pure substances, their specific gravity is quite constant. Calculating it provides a good way to distinguish between gems that have the same appearance. They may be of any size or shape, rough or cut, as long as they are unset.

A cubic centimeter of cold water weighs a gram. All gems are heavier than water, but they weigh less when suspended in water than they do in air, as a swimmer weighs less under the same circumstances, because he has displaced his own volume of water and is buoyed up by a force equal to the weight of the water that he displaces. The amount by which the gem decreases in weight is equal to the weight of the displaced water and indicates its relative density. The formula to be used involves two weighings; the weight of the stone in air is divided by the loss of weight in water. The specific gravity of diamond is 3.52, that is, it weighs a little over three and one-half times as much as the same volume of water. For this test the gem may be held in a coiled wire hung from a jeweler's balance. Specific gravity apparatus can be purchased if desired but home-made equipment is usually adequate.

Heavy liquids are often more convenient than scales. They make use of the principle that a gem will remain suspended in a liquid of the same density, will sink in a lighter liquid, and will float in a heavier one. Several chemicals are available for this purpose; bromoform, methylene iodide, and Clerici's solution are most often used. The simplest test of this kind requires only a glass of strong salt water in which amber and other natural resins float, whereas their plastic imitations (such as bakelite) drop to the bottom. By mixing several liquids, a *diffusion column*, which becomes heavier toward the lower part, can be prepared; a number of gems can be suspended in it at the same time, resting at different levels according to their specific gravities. Known gems called indicators may be used for comparison. Porous gems, including opal,

Specific Gravity Table

Cassiterite	7.00–6.80
Hematite	5.15–4.95
Pyrite	5.02–4.84
High zircon	4.72–4.68
Spessartite garnet	4.20–4.12
Almandite garnet	4.20–3.90
Low zircon	4.10–3.94
Corundum	4.01–3.99
Spinel	3.98–3.58
Andradite garnet	3.86–3.82
Pyrope garnet	3.82–3.68
Grossularite garnet	3.80–3.60
Chrysoberyl	3.72–3.70
Topaz	3.58–3.50
Diamond	3.53–3.51
Olivine	3.50–3.32
Jadeite jade	3.36–3.30
Spodumene	3.23–3.17
Fluorite	3.18
Tourmaline	3.12–3.00
Nephrite jade	3.02–2.90
Lapis lazuli	2.90–2.70
Beryl	2.85–2.65
Turquoise	2.85–2.60
Quartz	2.65
Orthoclase feldspar	2.57–2.55
Obsidian	2.47–2.33
Opal	2.20–2.00
Jet	1.34–1.30
Amber	1.09–1.05

turquoise, and pearl, should not be immersed in strong chemicals, and this test is not suitable for them.

Amber is the lightest gem; hematite and cassiterite are the heaviest, though zircon has the highest specific gravity of the major precious stones. Frequent lifting of gems, small though they are, gives one a surprising ability to identify many of them by this property alone. Typical values, with the range taken from G. F. Herbert Smith's *Gemstones*, are given on page 54.

Cohesion

The other essential attribute besides beauty and rarity that gives a substance value as a gem is *durability*—the capacity for standing up under the effect of abrasion, impact, and chemical action. Beauty, in other words, must be as permanent as possible. A few gems are always popular in spite of their lack of durability because their color is so pleasing. The two physical properties which determine the durability of a stone are *hardness* and *toughness*. These are often confused even by lapidaries. Hardness, as will be explained, is simply resistance to scratching; toughness or *tenacity* is resistance to breakage, either by cleavage, parting, or fracture. The property that combines both hardness and toughness is called cohesion, which is the force of electrical attraction that resists separation of the atoms and the ions.

Hardness

Hardness contributes greatly to the beauty of a gem, as well as to its durability. The brilliant luster that is so attractive a feature of diamond is largely made possible by the permanent polish that can be given to the stone. As everyone knows, diamond is the hardest of all substances and will scratch anything else. Designating diamond at one extreme as number 10, and the softest mineral, talc, at the other as number 1, a mineralogist named Frederich Mohs over a century ago proposed the *scale of hardness* still in common use. Here it is:

10	Diamond	5	Apatite
9	Corundum	4	Fluorite
8	Topaz	3	Calcite
7	Quartz	2	Gypsum
6	Feldspar	1	Talc

This scale is often misunderstood; it indicates the rank of hardness but not the amount of hardness. The tenth stone (diamond) is not twice as hard as the fifth (apatite), nor is number 9 (corundum) three times as hard as number 3 (calcite). In fact, the difference between diamond (10) and corundum (9) is far greater than the interval between corundum and the bottom of the series. What the table means is that a mineral will scratch any other listed below it, and will in turn be scratched by all those above it.

Number 7, quartz, marks a natural division between the harder and softer gems, because the dust and grit in the air contain countless particles of sand, which is pulverized quartz. Thus stones softer than number 7 will become dull with daily wear, losing their luster and their splendor, though opaque stones do not show the effect as conspicuously as transparent ones. It is desirable to remember, however, that the surface of most gems can be inexpensively restored by repolishing. The softer stones are quite satisfactory for neck and brooch ornaments since these are not subject to frequent abrasion. As contrasted both with natural stones and with their synthetic counterparts (which are very hard), the chief objection to glass imitations has always been the ease with which they become scratched and rounded after a little wear.

The hardness of crystalline gems varies with the crystal direction. In most stones these variations are of little consequence. One gem, kyanite, is so amazingly constituted that it can be scratched by a knife along the "grain" but not across it. The hardness of diamond depends upon the distance between the carbon atoms (the atomic structure is shown in Fig. 1), and study has shown the easiest direction for cutting to be parallel to a crystallographic axis. Inasmuch as each cube face is parallel to two axes, facets that are cut in that direction yield most readily; octahedron faces are equally inclined to all three of the axes but are parallel to none and so present the greatest opposition. Any difference in hardness among diamonds from different localities, especially Australia and Borneo (as stated by cutters), seems to be due to twinning or other irregularities in the structure rather than to variations in the actual diamond substance.

The hardness of practically all the gems except kyanite is characterized by its essential constancy; hence hardness would be one of the most useful tests for determining the identity of a gem except for the fatal drawback that a scratch may harm a cut gem, perhaps even setting up stresses that will eventually cause it to split. An imitation stone, attractive though it may be, is especially likely to become disfigured, and other tests have largely superseded the one for hardness. If the test is necessary, however,

Hardness Table

Diamond	10
Corundum	9
Chrysoberyl	8½
Topaz, spinel	8
Beryl, almandite garnet	7½
High zircon, pyrope garnet, grossu- larite garnet, spessartite garnet	7¼
Quartz, tourmaline, jadeite jade	7
Andradite garnet, olivine, nephrite jade, spodumene	6½
Opal	6½–5½
Feldspar, turquoise, low zircon	6
Lapis lazuli	5½
Sphene, apatite, variscite, obsidian	5
Fluorite, malachite	4
Coral	3¾
Pearl, sphalerite	3½
Jet	3
Amber	2½
Gypsum	2

the least conspicuous place on the gem should be selected; this is usually the widest part, called the "girdle," which can be covered later by the mounting. Care should be taken also to avoid mistaking the scratch from a harder substance for the powder left by a softer one. It is safer to use the unknown gem to scratch the other. Note should be made of the ease with which the scratch is secured; diamond, for instance, will gouge a ragged hole in a fragment of glass, whereas some other gem may produce only a fine line. Rough gems and crystals are quite appropriately tested for hardness, and for this purpose a set of standard mineral fragments, known as *hardness points*, may be advantageously used. Convenient approximations for hardness are made with the finger nail (2½ in the scale), a copper cent (3), a piece of window glass (5½), a knife blade (6), and a steel file (6½).

The hardness of most of the important gems is given in the table on page 58.

Cleavage

The infinitesimally small particles of which gem crystals are built are arranged in definite layers in three dimensions and are held together in their specific structural pattern or "lattice" by electrical attraction. Where the cohesion between layers is weakest, the stone under pressure or a blow will split in regular directions along its "grain"—this splitting is known as cleavage. In gems it can occur only in those that are crystalline minerals. Cleavage planes are always parallel to possible faces of the crystal; if such faces are not actually present, at least they may exist on some other crystal of the same species. Cleavage is often recognized by steplike chips on the surface of a gem or by parallel cracks in the interior. Even the kind of cleavage may sometimes be determined from the shape of these cracks.

Cleavage is described according to its quality and its direction. Thus "perfect octahedral" cleavage (typical of diamond and fluorite) is parallel to the octahedron faces in the isometric system and gives smooth, bright surfaces with facility. Again, "indistinct prismatic" cleavage yields an uneven surface roughly parallel to a prism face. After one becomes familiar with the "habits," or common forms, of crystals, he may sometimes recognize them in cut gems from the angles made by cleavage cracks.

The ready cleavage in diamond is utilized for splitting the crystal into convenient pieces for cutting. (See Fig. 63.) Topaz has a remarkable cleavage parallel to the base of the crystal, so that it can be split into thin plates more easily than a loaf of bread can be sliced. Kunzite (the lilac variety of spodumene) is exceedingly fragile because of its delicate cleavage in two directions; cutting a finished gem is a real triumph of the lapidary's art. Feldspar also cleaves in two directions almost at right angles to each other.

Parting

A sort of "false cleavage" is known as parting, and is usually due to minute secondary twinning. It is especially evident in corundum, which has a tendency to split in two directions, one of which is parallel to the base of the ruby or sapphire crystal, the other being inclined in a rhombohedral plane. Corundum separates, however, only in certain layers at definite intervals. This behavior distinguishes parting from true cleavage, which would take place along every layer in such directions.

Fracture

Amorphous gems have no cleavage and can break only with a fracture, which consequently has no regular direction. Crystalline gems may have both cleavage and fracture, although a strong cleavage tends to predominate over a possible fracture. Emerald is a conspicuous exception

60

because it fractures without difficulty but does not ordinarily cleave.

Fracture is described according to its appearance. The most distinctive variety in gems is *conchoidal* (Fig. 51), meaning shell-like, resembling the concentric arcs on shells and chipped glass. Quartz is characterized by this kind of

Fig. 51   Conchoidal Fracture in Obsidian
[From Longwell-Knopf-Flint *Outlines of Physical Geology*, 2nd edition, copyright 1941.]

fracture. Other fracture surfaces are called *splintery*, *uneven*, and *even*.

The difference between hardness (resistance to scratching) and toughness or tenacity (resistance to breakage) is shown by a number of hard stones, such as topaz and emerald, which are fragile and will shatter if struck. Most zircons (especially the popular blue, colorless, and golden ones), though reasonably hard, are brittle as a consequence of the heat treatment given to improve their color, and hence they have an unfortunate disposition to chip around the edges.

61

In contrast to gems that are rather easily cleaved or fractured, there are some that are tough in all respects. Jade is no harder than quartz, yet, because of its matted structure, a slab of it can be hurled against a wood floor without damage.

Electricity

The word electricity comes from the Greek word for amber, which the Greeks called *elektron*. The ability of amber after being rubbed to attract light fragments of material was noticed as early as 600 B.C. Other gems also develop enough static electricity by friction to catch small bits of paper. Diamond, tourmaline, and topaz show well this interesting property. Most gems must be polished in order to exhibit positive frictional electricity; diamond is practically the only exception and is positive whether rough or cut. Gems, except the few metallic ones, are nonconductors of electricity.

Tourmaline was brought to the attention of the Western world when some Dutch children found that the sun-heated stones attract and repel ashes and straws. Tourmaline was thus found to develop positive and negative electricity at opposite ends. The poles reverse themselves when the stone cools. Some jewelers have noticed that tourmaline jewelry displayed in warm windows becomes dustier than other kinds; this *pyroelectricity* is the reason.

Similar "polar" electricity is called *piezoelectricity* when the accompanying change in volume is caused by pressure instead of heat. Tourmaline crystals are used in submarines to register depth electrically because of their sensitivity to slight changes in pressure.

Reversing the procedure by the application of an alternating current of electricity to tourmaline causes it to change volume with such rapidity that it vibrates at high frequency. When the current corresponds to the natural frequency of the mineral, the vibration is greatly magnified. Plates of quartz, properly oriented and cut to proper thickness, vibrate with remarkable constancy. They are employed to maintain the wavelength of radio broadcasts. The variety and extent of their use for frequency control in electronics underwent a phenomenal growth during the Second World War.

Feel

An extremely delicate sense of touch is required to identify a gem by its texture. However, several of the minerals commonly used in carvings as substitutes for jade can be recognized in this manner. Steatite (soapstone) and agalmatolite are the best known; their softness causes them to feel soapy. Topaz seems to some persons to have a distinctive slippery feel which they ascribe to its wonderful polish.

Heat

Heat may be considered physical or chemical in effect —physical, when variations in temperature cause expansion and contraction which lead to breakage; and chemical, when some change occurs in the composition of the substance. Excessive heat will damage many gems by enlarging flaws or even creating them. At other times the color may be temporarily or permanently altered.

Opal contains a considerable amount of water and will crack as it dries; desiccation may be prevented by keeping it covered with a thin film of olive oil. Jewelers in dry climates, as in the American West, are familiar with this useful suggestion, and some of the finest opals ever sold in this country have been kept in oil swathes.

Tests involving heat are, for obvious reasons, even more limited than chemical tests in their application to gems. The blowpipe tests that are widely used in determinative mineralogy are suitable only for fragments. There are two gems, however, that may in uncut form be partly identified by the use of a simple flame. A rough piece of jet may be tested by holding an edge of it in the flame, which it makes sooty. Amber under the same conditions gives off an aromatic odor, as do several of its chief natural substitutes, though not the plastic imitations.

Minor Properties

Occasionally other properties besides those already discussed are of value in recognizing gems. Some of them occur rarely, but when observed they indicate with certainty the identity of the gem. Almost every precious stone has some characteristic that usually becomes familiar only after much experience in handling gems. Many such peculiarities represent delicately balanced combinations of optical properties. Others are structural or are due to the enclosure of foreign materials. The descriptions of individual gems in subsequent chapters of this book tell how their distinctive appearance is an aid to easier recognition.

Gems, like people, are known by the company they keep—and the homes they live in. So typical are the rock and mineral associates of some gems that the discovery of one of them invites a thorough search for the others. In 1870 the first diamond ever found in its original rock was discovered, and an ancient continent came to life again, because a man named DeKlerk noticed some garnet pebbles in a dusty South African stream bed and knew that the two gems are often found together. Suites of minerals, called *satellites*, accompany diamond in each of its localities. In river deposits they are sometimes referred to as *bantams*. Some of the minerals are themselves gemstones. Pyrope garnet, olivine, diopside, and zircon occur with diamond in the African pipes, and agate and olivine are typical of the stream deposits. Quartz, garnet, tourmaline, zircon, and corundum are found in the Brazilian diamond fields, where they are called *favas*.

Gems are formed in a variety of ways. Their history is a dramatic chapter of earth lore. To the creation of a mountain range, the eruption of a volcano, the bubbling of a hot spring, the flow of lava, the burial of a forest, even the crash of a shooting star—to each of these geologic events, and to others as well, gems owe their existence. Some modes of occurrence are, of course, more important than others. A knowledge of the types of rock in which a given gem is found often assists in recognizing it. The history of gem mining bears out Sydney H. Ball's observation that "gem discovery has progressively become less a matter of chance and more a result of trained technique."

Three main kinds of rock—igneous, sedimentary, and metamorphic—together constitute the outer part of the earth, called its crust.

Igneous rocks are formed by the cooling and solidification of *magma*, which is a hot solution of liquid and gas. When magma remains buried deep within the earth it loses heat slowly, and crystals are given sufficient time to grow to a visible size. On the contrary, when magma does not harden until it is close to the surface, or until it actually flows out upon the ground as lava, it cools too rapidly to yield conspicuous mineral grains; the final rock may be merely a natural glass such as obsidian. In either event the precise name of the rock produced depends upon its mineral and chemical composition, texture, color, and still other factors.

Kimberlite, the diamond-bearing rock of the South African volcanoes, is referred to as a *basic igneous rock* because it contains no quartz. *Acid igneous rocks*, on the other hand, contain specimens of quartz, enough surplus silica having been present to crystallize by itself.

In connection with deeply formed igneous rocks are *pegmatites*. To avoid confusion over the exact technical meaning, which has never been entirely agreed upon, it is adequate to say that pegmatites are the rocks (usually related to granite) that are noteworthy for their coarse texture and large crystals. They are probably the last part of a molten mass to solidify and they retain to the end considerable amounts of steam and other gases. When such rocks have penetrated cracks in adjacent rocks they

66

are known as *pegmatite dikes* or *veins*. Many rare minerals, including a wide variety of the most interesting gems, are found in pegmatites. For some gems, including rose quartz, moonstone, and smoky quartz, pegmatites are the only original source; for others, such as spodumene, they are the only important source. Because thick veins of white quartz often indicate the proximity of pegmatites, to which they are related, their existence should be noted at least with curiosity.

Even deeply buried rocks are at last uncovered by the forces of erosion. *Sedimentary rocks,* the second chief type of rock, are secondary in origin, having been derived from the decay and disintegration of earlier rocks. The weathered particles are carried by wind and glaciers, but mostly by streams, and deposited in layers. These sediments may settle out because of their weight, or they may be chemically precipitated out of solution.

Igneous or sedimentary rocks that have been considerably altered by heat, chemical reaction, or pressure become *metamorphic rocks,* the third main kind of rock. These may in turn become sedimentary rocks by being broken down, carried away, and redeposited. Garnet, lapis lazuli, and jade are among the typical metamorphic gems.

Gems may be found in the rocks in which they were formed. The rocks must be mined to recover the precious contents. Diamond pipes, emerald veins, jade quarries, and pegmatites are examples.

When gems are washed out of their native rock and transported by streams, their durability preserves them until they eventually come to rest, together with metals and other heavy minerals, as *placers* or *gravel deposits*. Such

67

sedimentary deposits usually yield gems with less cost and danger of breakage than hard rocks. Placers also have the advantage of high concentration, which makes them more profitable to operate. The rich and varied gem gravels of

Fig. 52   Large Geode Lined with Gem Crystals
[Ward's Natural Science Establishment.]

Ceylon, the alluvial diamond beds of Africa, and the sapphire fields along the Missouri River in Montana are typical. Ocean waters have concentrated amber along the shore of the Baltic Sea and diamonds on the west coast of Africa.

Geodes (Fig. 52) are hollow rocks of various sizes, lined with minerals, including quartz, opal, and chalcedony, which have settled out of solution. The myriad of small bright crystals nestling among larger ones aptly fit John Ruskin's description of "courtier crystals glittering in attendance upon others."

The evaporation of hot silica waters, such as flow from some springs, may leave gelatinlike material in the form of opal or chalcedony. Descending rather than rising mineral waters deposit turquoise in cracks in rock. Amber and jet, both gems of vegetable origin, are found in ancient sedimentary beds, where they were imprisoned for future ages.

A number of gem minerals, especially olivine and diamond, come to the earth in meteorites.

Climate plays a part in the occurrence of some gems. Turquoise may be looked for profitably only in dry regions, close to the surface of the ground. Olivine is so readily altered under atmospheric conditions that it is found only in fresh rock or as residual grains in desert country. Coral is notoriously sensitive to its environment, and water of constant temperature is requisite to its growth. The other gems of organic origin are also dependent on the factors that govern the growth of living things.

Chapter 3

Faceted Gems

John Ruskin expressed the point of view of the purist, and of the mineralogist as well, when he disapproved of disfiguring any crystal by subjecting it to the cutting and polishing process. But rare is the gem that cannot, for jewelry purposes, be improved in beauty through adequate lapidary treatment.

Pearl and staurolite are the only gems, in fact, that are worn in their natural state; however, the former is usually pierced for stringing into beads and the latter for hanging on a chain. Thus the art of the lapidary is involved in some manner in the use of all gems. This art at times becomes a science, dependent upon mathematical relationships which only secondarily have aesthetic significance.

In certain respects, moreover, the value of gems is largely determined by the perfection of their cutting. Poor work may ruin the finest stone, whereas skillful execution shows many inherent possibilities to best advantage.

Gems are classified in this book according to the style of cutting—*facet* or *cabochon*—to which they are most suited. *Faceted gems*, discussed in this chapter, are characterized by smooth flat surfaces or facets (from the

70

French word meaning "little face"). *Cabochon gems* (from the Latin word *caput* meaning "head") have rounded surfaces of varying degrees of curvature; the extension of the surfaces completely around a stone forms a bead. Combinations of both plane and rounded surfaces are also known. There are, in addition, carved and engraved stones fashioned as cameos, spheres, ornaments, and many other forms. Examples of the ingenuity that even an amateur lapidary may display are shown in Fig. 53.

Almost every gem appears in both major types of design. In general, transparent gems, whose beauty lies in their clearness, brilliancy, and fire, are selected for faceting, for only in this way are the desired properties fully revealed. The cabochon cuts, on the contrary, are more effective for opaque or translucent gems which have a pleasant color, show interesting mottling or markings, or possess unusual optical effects.

Ludwig van Berquem, of Flanders, is said to have discovered in the 15th century the advantages of placing symmetrical facets on diamond. Before that time cutters limited their efforts to covering the surface at random with many small flat patches, mostly for the purpose of concealing flaws. For approximately one hundred years, two styles of fashioning predominated—the *diamond point*, in which only the natural faces of the octahedron were polished, and the *table cut*, a more elaborate pattern also adapted from the original form of the crystal.

The *rose cut*, developed in a number of outlines, most of them with triangular facets, further improved the appearance of gems. It was regarded as quite satisfactory until the close of the 17th century, when Vincenti Peruzzi, of Venice, introduced the *brilliant cut*, which has, with

Fig. 53 Miniatures in Moss Agate Fashioned at Home by Lee M. Unruh, Salem, Oregon
[V. D. Hill.]

gradual minor changes, remained the standard for diamond cutting ever since. It revolutionized the gem industry by bringing out the real beauty of diamond and the brilliancy of other gems. At present the brilliant cut has 58 facets, 33 above the circular "girdle" and 25 below it, arranged in 8-fold symmetry. The names of the individual facets vary in different countries and languages. This style is the only one that has a scientific basis and is fully adequate to the optical properties of highly refractive stones. The *American cut*, planned originally by Henry Morse of Boston, is regarded as the most effective modification. Diamonds have lately been put on the market with numerous additional facets and a polished girdle. This is the Multi-Facet cut. The newer Princess cut has polished grooves to reflect the light.

When the outline of the brilliant cut is altered to meet the requirements of modern jewelry such forms as the boat-shaped *marquise* and the pear-shaped *pendeloque* are produced.

Colored gems are often cut in a generally square shape with a series of parallel facets leading both up and down from the girdle. Known as the *step, trap, cushion,* or *emerald cut,* this pattern is especially well suited to emerald, and many fine diamonds are cut similarly. Possible variations yield angular stones that are easily adaptable to current tastes. These have such descriptive names as *baguette, trapeze, epaulet, lozenge,* and *keystone.*

A distinction is made in the gem-cutting industry between shops that cut diamonds and those that fashion the other stones, since there is a vast difference in the hardness of the materials and the skill required. The technique of the lapidary, including his machinery, tools, and methods,

73

is explained in various books written for the amateur lapidary. Equipment for polishing flat surfaces on "slabs" is shown in Fig. 54, and Fig. 55 illustrates an adjustable holder for cutting facets.

The species of gems that are customarily cut in facet

Fig. 54   Lapidary Apparatus for Polishing Flat Surfaces
[United States National Museum.]

style are described in the rest of this chapter. Their sequence follows the arrangement of minerals given in the seventh edition of *Dana's System of Mineralogy*.[1]

[1] Palache, Berman, and Frondel, Harvard University. Published by John Wiley and Sons, Inc., New York. Volumes I–III, 1944–1962.

It was during the age of dinosaurs, about 60 million years ago, that a subterranean drama was enacted which was to change the history of the African continent. Ac-

Fig. 55   Mechanical Device for Faceting Gems

[M. D. Taylor.]

companied by violent explosions, enormous amounts of diamond-bearing volcanic rock were propelled upward, perforating the earth, which gave way before the irresistible force, and shattered rock filled the newly formed fissures.   Then the vigorous underground activity ceased,

75

but through succeeding ages the rain pelted down and the wind hurled itself against the ground, until, at the advent of man, all previous landscapes had long since disappeared, and in their place was the parched, monotonous African veldt, stretching in limitless desolation from rising to setting sun. Neither the natives nor the white man saw anything remarkable about the land, and farms were laid out and homes built in the few places where pioneers settled with their families. Diamonds to them were merely expensive baubles worn by the rich—luxuries associated with the splendor of the Orient, the refulgence of India, and the remoteness of Brazil. Nothing to interest hardworking Boers, thought they; so on they worked, and cleared their ground, and reared their children, and despised their English neighbors.

In 1867, while visiting some friends, Schalk van Niekirk was attracted by an unusual stone lying on the floor of the farmhouse and offered to buy it. He was laughingly told that it was but a child's plaything picked up in the field and that he should take it with him. Some time later the stone was shown to a mineralogist who identified it as a diamond worth several thousand dollars. There followed eager prospecting for other odd pebbles, but none was found for two years, until a shepherd boy discovered the magnificent "Star of South Africa," which he traded to van Niekerk for 500 sheep, 10 oxen, and a horse. It was later resold for $125,000.

Now began a wild diamond rush, as frantic and frenzied as any search for gold or oil. It centered about a number of places, first along the rivers and then inland where deposits were found in solid rock. The richest of these fields were the most crowded, and as the digging continued unabated the walls of the mines collapsed with ensuing death and terror. Order was finally restored by the action of several men who formed a combination by buying up the titles of the individual miners; this diamond trust—under the leadership of Cecil Rhodes, able successor to a long line of British empire builders—became one of the most powerful of the world's industrial corporations with vast ramifications under the beneficent stewardship of the Crown.

There are three distinct layers of rock in diamond mines. The top stratum is the *yellow ground*, so called from the color produced by oxidation, the cause of the decomposition that renders it easy to work. Beneath, of varying depth, is the *blue ground*; it has undergone partial alteration, weathering uniformly throughout, and disintegrates upon exposure to air, wind, and rain for about a year and frees its gemmy treasure. The blue ground is sometimes pierced by veins and dikes of *hardebank*, the third and least productive layer. The richness of the earth gradually diminishes; because the yellow ground has been depleted and the hardebank will not pay expenses, practically all the mining is done in the blue ground.

Shafts are sunk parallel to the *pipe* (as the neck of the former volcano is called; see Fig. 56) and tunnels are dug until they reach the pipe. The common operations involved in mining—drifting, stoping, drilling, blasting, slicing—are used. Piles of rock are then loaded (Fig. 57) onto trucks, each carrying 20 cubic feet, and moved over narrow rails to the storage bin, to be transferred later to the elevator or "skip" and raised to the top (Fig. 58).

Although, as mentioned, the blue ground yields its minerals after exposure to the weather—and this method of

77

Fig. 56 Wesselton Diamond Mine

This pipe mine near Kimberley is noted for the fine color of its diamonds. [DeBeers.]

Fig. 57   Kafirs Loading Blue Ground

Fig. 58   Washing Plant and Tailings Dump
Diamond Mining at Dutoitspan

[DeBeers.]

"farming" is used especially during times of depression— a more direct operation is available to hasten the day when the stones can be placed upon the market. The diamond-bearing rock is rolled and crushed in the jaws of great presses; then it is screened through coarse wire nettings which successively decrease in size until the material is no larger than a walnut. This is put into great circular washing pans, in which it is revolved and hurled against notched barriers which thrust the heavy minerals to the bottom, while the water and sand are drawn off through openings in the sides. After another series of screenings, the material is taken to the "jigs" or *pulsators*, in which the heavy minerals—meaning the valuable ones—are forced by plungers (see Fig. 59) through a layer of gravel which the lighter material cannot penetrate. A dense sludge now substitutes.

The remaining concentrate is then fed to the *grease tables* (Fig. 60)—slanted, rectangular sheets of metal, covered with a layer of petroleum jelly, and vibrating from side to side. The value of these tables lies in a peculiar property of diamond, which adheres immediately to grease but is untouched by water; as the stones roll down the incline, the diamond crystals are quickly caught, while the waste slides by, joining the "tailings" on the dump (Fig. 58). At intervals the tables are scraped clean and the diamonds are released by boiling, to be taken under guard to the offices, where they are sorted and graded for sale. Only an extremely minute portion of the blue ground finds its way here, for the richest mine ever known yielded at depth barely one part of diamond to 8 million parts of rock.

But a rough diamond is hardly worth going into ecstasies about, and the young man who attempted to present one

Fig. 59   Rotary Washing Pan

The heavy minerals are separated from the sand.

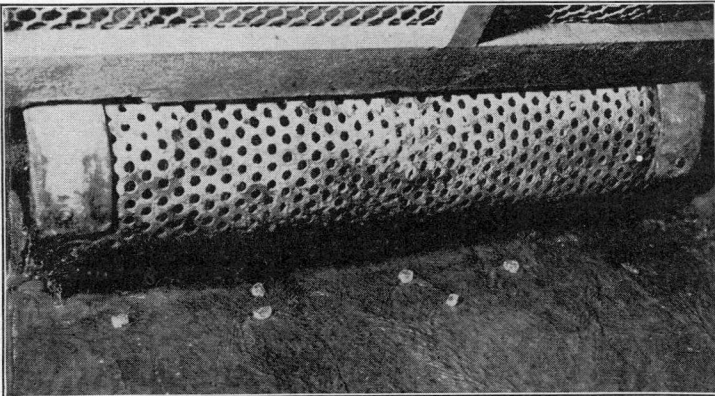

Fig. 60   Grease Table

Diamond is the only mineral caught by the grease.

Diamond Concentrating Methods

[DeBeers.]

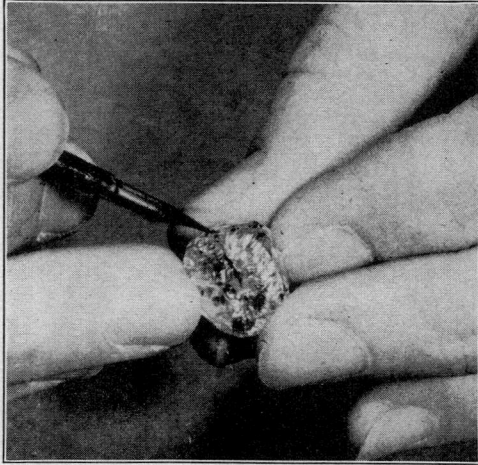
Fig. 61   Marking

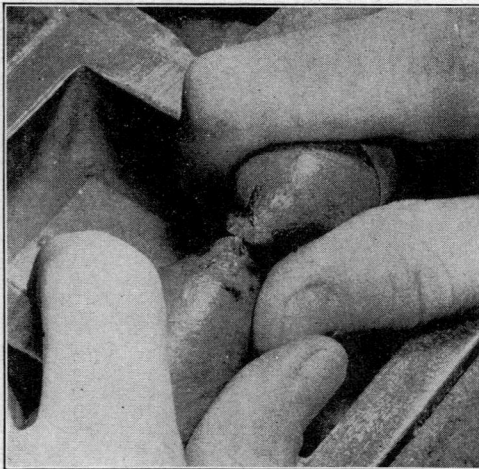
Fig. 62   Notching
Early Steps in the Diamond Cutting Process

[DeBeers.]

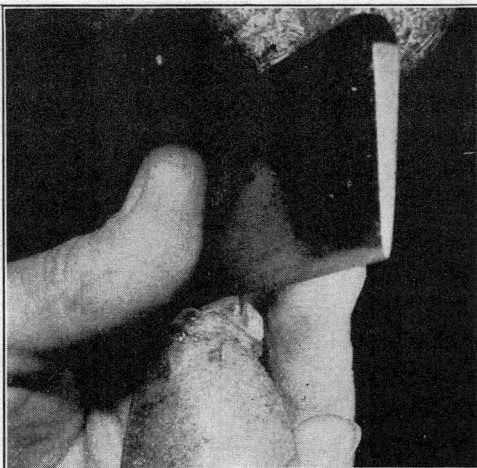

Fig. 63   Cleaving

Fig. 64   Sawing

[DeBeers.]

83

Fig. 65   Rounding

Fig. 66   Faceting
Later Steps in the Diamond Cutting Process
84   [DeBeers.]

Fig. 67   Sorting Diamonds

Fig. 68   Ten Days' Production

[DeBeers.]

85

to the lady of his dreams would be fortunate to escape with minor cuts and abrasions. A well-designed diamond is a scientific as well as an artistic achievement; the facets must be of a certain number and of a definite size and shape, each bearing to the others a relationship determined by the laws of optics. Indian lapidaries were the first to fashion diamonds, but they merely removed the outer "skin" from the natural crystal faces or added small facets to disguise the presence of flaws.

Five major steps are involved in the cutting process, and all must be done by experts, specialists in their work. The least spectacular phase, but in some ways the most important, is done by the *marker*, who outlines in india ink (Fig. 61) those parts of the crystal which are to be removed and those which are to be utilized, according to the size, shape, color, and quality of each stone. After notching (Fig. 62), the first shaping is done by the *cleaver*, who makes use of the pronounced cleavage, by means of which diamond may be split easily (Fig. 63) in any one of four directions. Cutting against the grain requires the work of the *sawyer*, who places the stone in a shell-like holder called a "dop," and slits it with a speedily revolving bronze disk covered with a mixture of diamond dust and oil (Fig. 64). The rough stone is then given a circular form by the *cutter*, who sets it in a lathe and rounds off the edges with a diamond-pointed tool (see Fig. 65). The facets are placed on the stone by the *polishers*, who work in turns, the first group shaping the 18 most important surfaces and the second group completing the other 40. Faceting is done on horizontally revolving iron wheels treated with the same compound of crushed diamond and oil that is used for

86

sawing; the stone is held against the wheel by a dop set at the proper angle, as shown in Fig. 66.

Inasmuch as diamond is cut so slowly that it polishes itself (the only gem that does) no further treatment is needed except cleaning in boiling acid. Only sorting (Fig. 67) and marketing remain, although some dealers may assert that the latter is the most formidable task of all. There, in a folded paper, lies a thing of rare loveliness—a mass of glittering light, a scintillating glow of varied colors, now separating into tints of spectral purity, now blending into the splendor of a twinkling star. (See Fig. 68.) It is a diamond, some day to be owned by an Indian maharajah, worn by an English duchess, or placed on the left hand of an American girl.

Alluvial Deposits

The mining methods just described are employed only in the primary volcano or pipe deposits, which are relatively restricted in distribution. Prior to the discovery of the first pipe the world's supply of diamonds had always come from secondary sources—shallow *alluvial* or *placer deposits* where the gems were concentrated with other heavy and resistant minerals in stream beds, river terraces, and sedimentary formations, mostly through the process of rock decay and the action of running streams. All the famed Indian and Brazilian fields had been secondary sources. Upon the opening in 1926 and 1927 of several large African deposits in Lichtenburg and Little Namaqualand, the alluvial type again became the most important. During the past four decades alluvial mines

87

have yielded all but a few per cent of the total (mostly now, however, outside the Republic of South Africa).

Obtaining diamonds from such surface workings is much simpler and less expensive than mining far underground. The deepest mine, the Kimberley, was operated below 4,000 feet, and even the most productive pipe contains diamonds only sparsely. Moreover, the alluvial stones are generally of better quality because those with the most flaws had been broken up during the journey from their place of origin.

The alluvial deposits of Africa are widely scattered through the southern half of the continent. Some are located along the Atlantic Ocean beaches and may even have come from areas now buried beneath the sea. Angola, Sierra Leone, Congo, and Ghana fields contribute most of the alluvial diamonds; the Republic of South Africa has lost its former predominance, although its placer and pipe mines combined give it first rank in terms of value. The Congo is, by weight, the largest producing country, but most of its output is industrial stones. One of the Bécéka mines is the richest in the world. An interesting feature of these alluvial fields is the presence of artifacts from primitive cultures, showing their geologic recency.

Among the most famous of the South African diamond mines are the Dutoitspan, Bultfontein, DeBeers, Jagersfontein (noted for its high-quality stones), Wesselton, and Premier (the largest of all). The Williamson mine in Tanganyika is, however, the largest on the entire continent. Mining diamonds at sea is a new innovation in South-West Africa; the stones seem to have come from offshore deposits.

Indian Deposits

India was the first source of diamond and from there have come most of the historically famous stones. Tradition puts the discovery at about 5,000 years ago but that is probably twice as long as the actual time. The mines were exceedingly successful, reaching their peak in the 17th century; the marketing center was Golconda, a name which even today is a synonym for fabulous wealth. Golconda is in the former state of Hyderabad.

Other Foreign Deposits

As the yield in India rapidly declined virtually to the point of exhaustion, diamonds were found in Brazil about 1720, and that country maintained its supremacy until surpassed by the African mines a century and a half later. The states of Minas Gerais, Matto Grosso, and Bahia produce most of the Brazilian diamonds, generally in a quite primitive way.

Diamond is no stranger to still other countries. Notable stones have for a thousand years come from the western part of Borneo, where even during the Japanese conquest they were mined by Chinese and Malay prospectors from hundreds of small shafts in the jungle. Australian diamonds have appeared at intervals from New South Wales. British Guiana fields promise much for the future when they become more accessible. Private capital is beginning to develop fields in Venezuela, where government plans for exploitation had previously failed. The Soviet Union may soon enter the ranks of the leading diamond-producing nations, but statistics are not available; the present output from the Ural Mountains is said to be twenty times the pre-war yield.

United States Deposits

Diamonds occur in Arkansas in a pipe that is remarkably similar in structure and composition to those of South Africa. Many fine crystals, the largest weighing 40 carats, have since 1906 come from this area near Murfreesboro in Pike County. High cost of production has limited the output of the property, which is now operated as a tourist attraction under the name Crater of Diamonds. Here you may search for diamonds yourself and keep the small ones you find. Occasional scattered diamonds have been picked up in a number of other states but their original source is unknown. The largest and most recent, announced in 1943, is the 34-carat Punch Jones diamond, which was found in 1928 while a youngster and his father were pitching horseshoes in a vacant lot in Peterstown, West Virginia.

Marketing

Most of the diamond-mining companies of the world belong to the Diamond Corporation (known to most jewelers by its old name, the Syndicate), to which they sell their output. DeBeers Consolidated Mines, Ltd., is the largest supplier and also owns most of the stock. Each company has an allotted quota which is varied from time to time according to its prospects for production, so that the whole system of control is at once a strong and yet remarkably flexible monopoly. Not all these African companies are British, as is commonly believed, and some operate on French, Belgian, and Portuguese territory. A few minor producers in other parts of the world do not belong to the corporation but often find it advantageous to co-operate in maintaining the price. Through its subsidiary, the Diamond Trading Company, the corporation disposes of the rough gemstones to brokers and cutters from offices in London and Kimberley.

Name

The word diamond comes from the Greek word meaning "unconquerable," referring to its extreme hardness and to the erroneous belief that it could not be broken.

Crystals

Diamond crystals show the common forms of the isometric system, corresponding to the atomic structure shown in Fig. 1. The most prominent forms are the octahedron (resembling a double pyramid), the dodecahedron, and the cube. The table of the cut stone is usually placed almost, though not exactly, parallel to a natural face of the crystal; and (as explained previously in the section on "Hardness") the easiest directions of cutting are those most nearly along a crystallographic axis.

Diamond is crystallized carbon; the gem varieties are practically pure. Nothing in nature, however, is absolutely flawless and diamond is no exception. The flaws are usually spots of liquid compounds of carbon which

91

failed to harden as the mineral was formed. In some stones, but in only about one per cent of the entire production, the flaws remain so small that they are not visible with a pocket magnifier.

The other form of carbon is graphite, a mineral so different from diamond that their relationship is almost unbelievable. Graphite is the soft black substance used as pencil "lead," stove polish, and a lubricant. Even stranger is the fact that it is really the more stable form of carbon, because diamond changes to graphite at excessively high temperatures.

Several kinds of diamond crystals are known, according to their different atomic structures. Some conduct electricity. Nuclear radiation can be measured with great accuracy by others.

Famous Diamonds

Through the display of glass replicas at world fairs and in jewelers' windows, the appearance and names of the famous diamonds of history have become popularly familiar. Ten of the best known are pictured in Fig. 69. South Africa has furnished the largest stones, climaxed by the Cullinan, a giant of 3,106 carats, the size of a man's fist. A number of large diamonds, among which are several that have attained newspaper headlines, have been discovered during recent years. The Jonker, found in the Transvaal in 1934, had a superb clarity and weighed 726 carats before it was cut into 20 stones. The Vargas diamond, named for the former president of Brazil, in whose

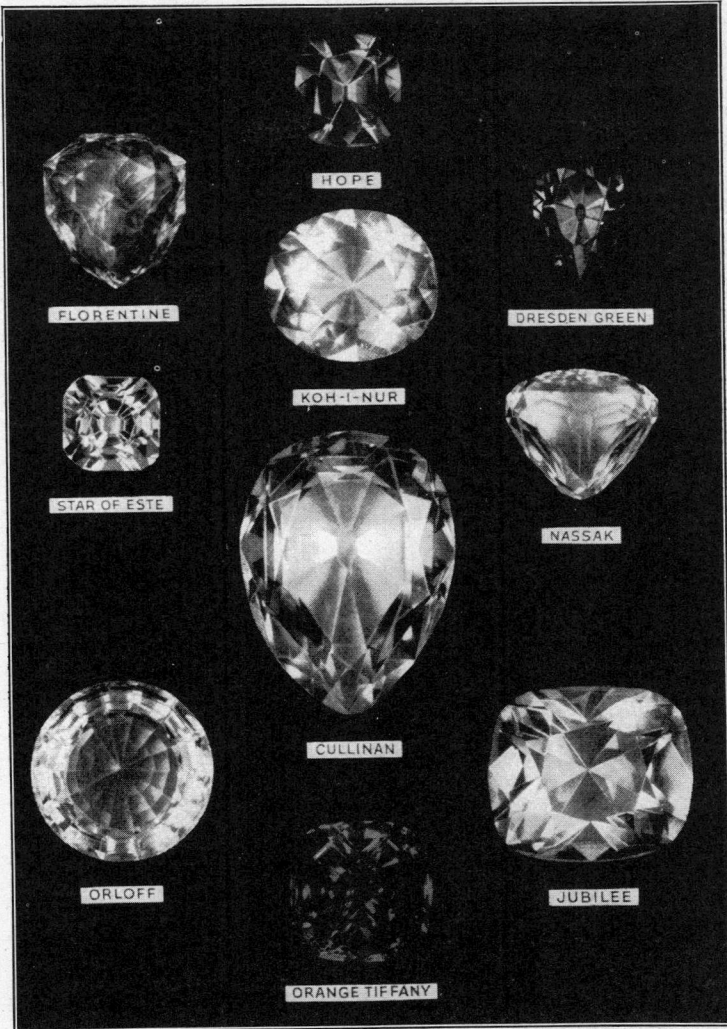

FLORENTINE

HOPE

DRESDEN GREEN

KOH-I-NUR

STAR OF ESTE

NASSAK

CULLINAN

ORLOFF

JUBILEE

ORANGE TIFFANY

Fig. 69 Some Famous Diamonds

[N. W. Ayer and Son.]

country it was found, exceeded the Jonker in weight by only 1 carat and was cut into 29 stones. The largest Venezuelan diamond is El Libertador, found in 1942 and named to honor Simon Bolivar, the liberator of most of South America; it has been fashioned into 3 emerald-cut stones. A diamond of 770 carats, the largest of all alluvial diamonds, was found in Sierra Leone, Africa, in 1945.

Colors

Few diamonds are entirely devoid of color; those having a bluish tint are more desirable than yellow ones because of their greater rarity, although yellow diamonds are frequently more brilliant. The commercial term "blue white," so often misused today, properly means a gem showing no color in daylight except blue, and these are by no means common. Stones of a distinct hue, on the other hand, are called fancy diamonds and bring a good price. Red and deep blue are the rarest colors. The blue Hope diamond, weighing 44 carats, was given to the Smithsonian Institution in 1958. The 129-carat Tiffany Yellow has been displayed in public for a long time; its color is inclined toward orange.

Cutting Centers

The collapse of the diamond industry of the Lowlands was one of the dramatic events of the war. Antwerp in Belgium and Amsterdam in the Netherlands have for centuries been the chief cutting centers; Antwerp alone consumed more "rough" than the rest of the world. The Diamond Corporation had been careful to send few stones abroad after the war began. With the German invasion the situation was demoralized, though many of the cutters escaped and were mainly responsible for the rapid growth of the industry in a dozen other countries. Since the termination of hostilities the Belgian lapidaries showed a remarkable economic recovery, followed somewhat later by the Dutch.

The United States, the Republic of South Africa, and the Netherlands are today the chief cutters of large stones, and Belgium, Israel, and Cuba cut most of the small sizes. Prices have advanced in accordance with the increase in labor costs in the new places; the smaller stones have risen by far the most. New York is the center of American production, and half a dozen other cities house important diamond-cutting plants. Mechanization may determine the extent to which the United States can retain its present share of moderate-sized stones, although the large stones have been cut here profitably for many years.

Industrial Diamonds

The earliest industrial use for diamond was to cut other diamonds. The next use was for glass cutting. Today there are so many indispensable applications that our vast industrial machine would be practically halted without them. Most are used for truing grinding wheels; nothing else will so effectively dress wheels of emery, Carborundum, and cemented tungsten and boron carbides. Many are used to turn machine tools; the important development of the *bonded diamond wheel* for this purpose has occurred

95

largely since the beginning of World War II. Such wheels made it possible to grind American cartridge dies in one-third of the previous time. Tungsten for light-bulb filaments, copper, and other metals are drawn into wire through *diamond dies*. The electrical equipment of a single bomber may include 10,000 feet of wire, all of which must be drawn through diamonds. A diamond-die industry, which centered in France and Switzerland before the war, was hastily created in the United States to meet the emergency. Drilled diamonds are used also in oil nozzles for furnaces. *Diamond core drills* are important in mining and oil-well operations. Stoneyards employ steel saws up to seven feet in diameter and containing perhaps a thousand diamonds to cut granite and marble. Diamonds are also used in phonograph needles; in optical and dental drills; in etching tools for the artist; and for turning ivory, hardwood, and plastics into a wide range of articles from bowling balls to doorknobs. Strategic mineral, to be sure!

During the war, profits from the sale of gem diamonds enabled the producers to maintain a lower price level for the much-needed industrial stones than if the mines had been operated for them alone. Except the small yield in Borneo and some smuggling from South America, the allied nations had almost complete control over the output of industrial diamonds. Since the spring of 1946 the Diamond Corporation has sold its industrial stones through a new subsidiary, Industrial Distributors (1946), Ltd.

Three varieties of industrial diamond are known. *Bort* is an aggregate of many tiny crystals without definite orientation; this term is also loosely used for poor fragments of actual gem type. *Carbonado* or black diamond

96

also has an aggregate structure but of a different kind and is highly valued for drills; it is found almost exclusively in Brazil. *Ballas* consists of a radial mass of small crystals, which is very durable because it does not cleave easily. Uniformity of grading the diamond powder used in cutting diamonds has been secured in the United States by the adoption of commercial standards. The invention of synthetic diamond has opened up a whole new source of this valuable material, encouraging the further use of diamonds, both natural and artificial, in heavy industry. Theoretically, no substance can be harder than diamond under the conditions of pressure and temperature that prevail at the surface of the earth.

Origin

The origin of diamond is still a mystery. A number of elaborate theories have been propounded but none of them fits all the conditions known to exist in the pipe mines, which are the only certain original deposits. The particular rock in which these mines are dug is called *kimberlite*. The diamond crystals may have formed at great depths in some other rock, which became broken off or engulfed by the new volcanic material which then forced it upward. They may, however, have formed in the kimberlite itself during or after its actual rise in the pipe. Or they may have been a part of the kimberlite when it was deep in the crust of the earth.

Enormous amounts of heat and pressure have generally been assumed to be necessary for the creation of diamond.

97

This has been proved by the success of the makers of synthetic diamond. Earlier, most of the experimenters put their faith in the development of pressure alone. This did not work. Both pressure and heat are necessary. In addition, the presence of a metallic catalyst (to cause the chemical reaction to proceed favorably) seems to be required; this may be nickel.

CORUNDUM

Few persons would believe by eye examination alone that two stones of such contrasting colors as ruby and sapphire are alike in all other respects. One, vivid in flaming red; the other, restful in the lustrous blue of the twilight sky—both are varieties of corundum which differ mainly in color. When the red and the blue combine they form a violet or amethyst sapphire. Indeed, practically every hue has been found, and there may even be several colors in adjacent layers in the same crystal. Corundum is the mineral family or species; ruby and the many sapphires are the varieties.

Diamond is the only gem that is harder. Ruby and sapphire, possessing in addition to hardness the advantage of having absolutely no cleavage (though there is a parting) and showing but a slight tendency to fracture, are therefore about the most durable of ring stones. They are heavy gems, as their high specific gravity indicates. They are brilliant gems with a high refractive index.

Chemically, corundum is an oxide of aluminum; traces of

other metallic oxides furnish the wide range of colors. Mineralogically, sapphire is the name given to all corundum gems except the red variety, ruby. Popularly, it is the

Fig. 70 Sapphire Crystals from Ceylon
[Ward's Natural Science Establishment.]

name applied to the blue corundum alone. However, the stones sold as "Oriental amethyst," "Oriental emerald," etc., are really sapphires of the lesser-known but equally

99

beautiful colors. The adjective indicates their original association with Asia.

Corundum belongs to the hexagonal system. Its familiar shape is the long, doubly tapered crystal, shown in the drawing of Fig. 17 and the sapphires of Fig. 70, but most crystals of ruby tend to be short and stubby.

Ruby

The exotic barbarity of its color has associated ruby with the passion of the Orient. Few other gems have been called upon to express so much symbolism. Following the traditions of the Poles and the Russians, American gem dealers have appropriately designated ruby as the birthstone for July. Surely its fiery red is like the summer sun.

The romance of ruby is intimately concerned with the story of India, where the stone was probably first worn in jewelry. There, on "Mother India's" eastern border, in the republic of Burma, are found the finest rubies in the world. The exceedingly rare "pigeon's blood" color—deep carmine slightly tinged with blue—is obtained especially in the Mogok Stone Tract and in the near-by Kathe district, which are both about one hundred miles north of Mandalay and a lesser distance west of Lashio, the southern terminus of the Burma Road.

Control of the mines was secured in 1597 by the king of Burma, who is said to have exchanged a piece of worthless territory for the precious land and thus become "Lord of the Rubies." Successive rulers leased the workings to licensed miners who paid rent both in money and in stones. All gems over a certain size were forfeited to the king, and consequently more than one fine stone was broken

100

to evade the law. The finding of a large ruby was the occasion for a national celebration, and the stone was escorted from the mine to the throne by a guard of uniformed soldiers. About eighty years ago the mines were leased by a French company, but upon the annexation of Upper Burma by the British an English firm was granted the concession, and Burma Ruby Mines, Ltd., was formed, which marketed its product in London.

Native methods of recovering the ruby are quite primitive. A shaft is sunk to the gem-bearing earth, which is hauled to the surface in baskets; the rubies are separated by washing, then sorted and graded. Different systems are used in the wet and the dry seasons. Large investments for machinery were made by the British, but the loss of money was so great that hand methods were restored. The production varied from year to year, sometimes one or two large rubies accounting for almost the entire output. Formal operation of the Burmese mines ceased long before the war and the Japanese seizure of the area, but the local inhabitants continued to work the deposits in simple fashion until they were flooded and bombed.

Ruby of a paler color is found with sapphire in the gem gravels of Ceylon. A district in Siam known as The Hills of Precious Stones has been an important source of darker ruby since early days. In both places sapphires far outnumber rubies, however. Other less important sources are Rhodesia and Afghanistan.

Because corundum of every color except red is called sapphire, the gradual transition from ruby to pink sapphire makes the naming of a light-red specimen a matter of individual interpretation. Both the red of ruby and the green of emerald are believed to be due to an oxide

101

of chromium, the chemical having a different structure in each of the two gems. A strange phenomenon is that ruby will turn green if heated to a high temperature and will retain its new color until almost cool again. Presumably, when exposed to heat, the chromium temporarily takes on the state that it normally has in emerald. Iron oxide may contribute to the color of ruby, and radium radiation may possibly assist in producing the finest hue. The color, which varies from rose to purplish, holds well under artificial light; the best aspect may be obtained by careful cutting of the rough stone.

Some ruby when cut with a rounded top displays a six-rayed star across the surface, like that shown by star sapphire, but *star rubies* are much rarer.

The word ruby comes from the Latin *ruber* meaning "red" and at one time was used to indicate every stone of that color. Even today the term is sometimes misappropriated and red garnet is sold by such deceptive names as "Cape ruby" and "Arizona ruby."

Sapphire

Esteemed greatly by the ancients, sapphire even today has lost none of its appeal to lovers of beauty. Mirroring the serenity of an autumn sky, blue sapphire is a perfect choice for September's birthstone. The other colors of the gem, furthermore, are of a seemingly endless variety, although as yet the blues are the only ones that are well known.

The original meaning of the word is uncertain; it perhaps had an astrologic connotation. It is usually given as "blue," which accurately describes the opaque blue stone (speckled with gold) which we call lapis lazuli, and we are now confident that this was the sapphire of olden times. However, the true sapphire became known by the time of the New Testament and was probably the stone called jacinth in *Revelation*.

There are a number of famous sapphires with interesting stories. One of the finest rough stones is the Rospoli sapphire, a perfect crystal found in India by a native spoonmaker. In the British Museum there is an image of Buddha carved from a single stone. Until several years ago the largest sapphire ever known was among the lost treasures of an Oriental king; but even it has been surpassed by the Gem of the Jungle. This tremendous stone was found when a bolt of lightning uprooted a tree which had concealed it. Weighing 958 carats in the rough, it was bought by an American dealer for over $100,000 and cut into 9 stones, the largest of which weighed more than 66 carats.

The most valuable sapphire is a rich, velvety, cornflower or royal blue. Montana sapphires are an appealing "electric blue" found in no other gem. Orange, yellow, green, and purple sapphires are also wonderfully beautiful. Pink sapphire merges into true ruby. The odd name *padparadschah* refers to a golden-red variety, more often seen, however, in synthetics than in nature.

Star sapphire has been among the most popular of gemstones during recent years. When cut with a rounded top it exhibits a six-rayed star across its surface. This feature is due to a peculiar crystal structure which reflects the light in such a way that a complete star is formed. The star is an inherent part of the stone, so that a gem may be cut into any number of smaller ones, yet if prop-

103

erly oriented each will contain a whole star. The wearer of such a stone has indeed a unique gem. Fortunately, many of the less expensive colors show the clearest stars. An approach to transparency is much to be desired, but complete transparency is impossible in a star stone.

The Orient is the home of the sapphire. Siam yields at least half (and much the better half) of the world's supply, chiefly from an area on the Gulf of Siam extending somewhat into Cambodia. India furnishes most of the larger stones; during a brief but spectacular career in the late 19th century the province of Kashmir produced the most glorious sapphires ever seen. Emphasis should be placed on the many superb sapphires, including the star variety, that come from the island of Ceylon. Neighboring Burma is also an important but little-appreciated source. Australia (although its stones are dark) and Montana are other significant sources. In fact, sapphires from Fergus County, Montana, mined by a British firm and shipped for cutting to Europe, were the result of the most intensive gem-mining project ever carried on in the United States. The need for bearings for war instruments was primarily responsible for the recent revival of the Montana industry, although some gem material has also been obtained.

SPINEL

Spinel occupies a curious position in the world of gems. The genuine stone is hardly known under its own name, since it resembles ruby and sapphire, occurs with them in the same deposits, and is often confused with them in selling. The synthetic spinel, also, is usually called by some other name according to its particular color, and many a pretty ring is set with a synthetic spinel instead of the gem that it is supposed to contain.

Several magnificent gems which had been thought for centuries to be rubies have been proved recently to be spinels. One of these, known as the Black Prince's ruby, is the large oval stone in the front of the British Imperial State Crown. It was given to the Black Prince by Pedro the Cruel in the 14th century, and was later worn by Henry V on the helmet which saved his life at the battle of Agincourt. Another superb red spinel among the British crown jewels is the Tribute of the World. It is the largest in existence. Changing owners as a result of successive conquests over a period of 500 years, it was finally presented to Queen Victoria after the Indian wars, but its identity was made known only from the ancient Persian inscriptions engraved upon it.

Spinel is hard and durable, well suited to the most intensive wear. It crystallizes in the isometric system in sharp octahedrons resembling two pyramids joined base to base (Fig. 71), or in twinned crystals placed side by side. It has a variable chemical composition and is regarded either as an aluminate of magnesium or as a multiple oxide of magnesium and aluminum. The magnesium may be replaced by a considerable amount of ferrous iron or manganese, and the aluminum by ferric iron or chromium. Most gem spinel, however, is essentially pure, although some blue stones do contain a small percentage of zinc.

The colors of spinel span the rainbow. Red stones resemble ruby and are colored by the same chemical, chromium oxide. *Rubicelle* is the orange-red variety; such

105

a choice-quality flame spinel brings a high price. The familiar term "balas ruby," applied to the pink and rose-colored spinel, is of course a misnomer. Blue spinel has an interesting steely color and is rare. *Almandine spinel*

Fig. 71   Octahedral Crystals of Spinel from Orange County, New York

[From Hawkins *The Book of Minerals*, copyright 1935.]

has the purplish-red color of the true almandite (which, however, is a garnet). Several of the spinel varieties are not transparent but show good colors. These include the green *chlorospinel* (containing ferric iron), the brownish *picotite* (containing chromium), and the almost-black *ceylonite* or *pleonaste* (containing ferrous iron).

Spinel has always been found with the corundum gems in Burma, Siam, and Ceylon, which are still the chief producing localities. For a thousand years good stones came from metamorphic deposits in Afghanistan visited by Marco Polo.

CHRYSOBERYL

The varieties of the species chrysoberyl are so strangely unlike one another in appearance that merely looking at them gives one little indication of their close relationship. But the scientist, with ingenuity and perseverance, finds that the differences between them are rather superficial, and that their fundamental characteristics are much the same. Lovers of the beautiful and the romantic find chrysoberyl to be among the most fascinating of gems, both for its appeal to the eye and for its intriguing story.

The name, meaning "golden beryl," indicates the original idea of the identity of this stone, but it is now known to have no connection with beryl except that both contain the rare element beryllium and the common element aluminum. Chrysoberyl is classed either as a multiple oxide of beryllium and aluminum or as an aluminate of beryllium. Other chemicals (iron and chromium) present as a replacement are responsible for the interesting colors. Unless twinned, as shown in Fig. 2, the crystals of chrysoberyl are rather ordinary looking (Fig. 22), sometimes having six sides, although they belong to the orthorhombic and not the hexagonal system. Very important is the great hardness, which is exceeded by only two other minerals, diamond and corundum.

Here is a pair of jeweler's tweezers. Let us pick up these stones, one at a time, and learn why they have for so long thrilled gem connoisseurs.

107

Alexandrite

Alexandrite has been called "an emerald by day, an amethyst by night." It is green when viewed in daylight but turns raspberry or columbine red under artificial light, the change being due to different color absorption which varies according to the kind of illumination. Alexandrite was discovered in Russia a century ago on the day that the future czar Alexander II became of age and was named after him. Oddly enough, its twin colors were those of the Imperial Guard, and for a time the stone was not found outside Russia.

Ceylon is the source of most present-day alexandrite, which is mined there from placer deposits. Fine stones are rare and give promise of becoming even scarcer. The artificial stones represented as alexandrite are either glass, synthetic corundum, or synthetic spinel, and are described in Chapter 7. (There are no true synthetic alexandrites having the same composition and properties as the natural gem.) The synthetics are more bluish in daylight and lack the rich hues and dramatic color changes which make a fine alexandrite one of the most appealing of Nature's treasures.

Cat's-Eye

No greater contrast to an alexandrite could be imagined than a cat's-eye, with its mysterious band of light which glides across the rounded surface of the gem as it is moved from side to side, exactly like the eye of a living cat. Cat's-eye has long been held in high esteem by the Moors and the Hindus, who believe that it protects wealth and even causes it to increase in value. Natives of Ceylon consider it a charm against evil spirits. British royalty has favored the gem for engagement rings.

The shifting light of cat's-eye is called *chatoyancy*. It is caused by reflection of light from great numbers of very small hollow canals, as many as 65,000 to the inch, arranged parallel to the main axis of the crystal. To show the effect to best advantage, the gem must be cut with a curved top, similar in shape to a coffee bean, with the canals running across the width of the surface; the "pupil" of the eye then appears down the length of the stone at right angles to these canals. The narrower and sharper the line, the better the gem is considered to be.

Apple green, honey yellow, and dark green are the most highly prized background colors of cat's-eye. Variously contrasting bands add to their beauty. In the Marlborough collection was a splendid gem carved into a lion's-head cameo, with shifting shades of light that gave an amazingly lifelike appearance. Another magnificent cat's-eye was among the crown jewels of the king of Kandy and was later placed in the Hope collection. It is so cut that the natural markings in the stone resemble an altar lighted by a torch.

Cymophane (meaning "wave of light") is a name applied by some gemologists to those cat's-eyes which, instead of a sharply defined streak, show a hazy floating light. The same names, however, are frequently used interchangeably for both kinds.

Most of the world's supply of cat's-eye comes from Ceylon, the "jewel case of the Orient." Brazil is another source.

A variety of quartz, somewhat similar in appearance to the chrysoberyl gem, is called cat's-eye by many persons, but it lacks the rich beauty of the chrysoberyl variety and brings only a moderate price. This quartz cat's-eye and a closely related stone called tiger's-eye are discussed among the gems of the silica group in Chapter 5.

Countless thousands of "Chinese cat's-eyes" were sent home from South Pacific islands during the war, or were set in rings, bracelets, and pins that were made by hand on the spot. These attractive "stones" are really the lids of snail (gastropod) shells, and of course have no kinship with any mineral cat's-eye. Such a calcareous plate, with a dome-shaped top and the luster of porcelain, comes in various colors and is called an *operculum*.

Other Chrysoberyls

Another variety of chrysoberyl is unlike those already mentioned. It has no such unusual optical properties but is a transparent, usually pale, yellowish-green gem with a pleasing luster. Its name is *chrysolite chrysoberyl*, the word chrysolite being derived from the Greek meaning "golden stone." The leading sources are Brazil, Ceylon, and Rhodesia.

Chrysoberyl occurs also in lovely clear greens, yellows, and browns which make attractive, though little-known, gems. Excellent lemon-yellow stones come from Brazil; light-green ones, also from that country, seem to have a promising future. Bright colorless crystals have recently been found in Ghana in Africa and in the ruby mines of Burma.

The radiant flash of rainbow colors that is the essence of diamond is surpassed three-fold by that of the well-known mineral but little-appreciated gem, sphalerite. Inasmuch as its dispersion is 300 per cent greater, the spectra are three times as wide as those in diamond. Their intensity, however, is weakened by the diluting effect of the yellowish-brown body color of the gem against which they appear. Such an amazing characteristic, nevertheless, combined with a bright (though tending toward resinous) luster and a fine brilliancy, raises the question as to why sphalerite is not used more often in jewelry. Cut specimens are sought eagerly for collections, but the physical properties seriously violate the requirements for a jewelry stone. Sphalerite is entirely too soft, and its sensitive six-way cleavage makes it difficult to cut and susceptible to easy breakage.

The very scarcity of transparent material would prevent sphalerite from becoming familiar enough to create its own demand—rarity is not always a virtue. Except some from Mexico and Spain, little sphalerite of gem quality has been found.

In its common brown-to-black form, however, sphalerite is a widespread mineral. Composed of zinc sulfide, it supplies most of the world's zinc. Miners call the ore "rosin jack" (in allusion to the luster) or "blackjack," and the British refer even to the gem as *zinc blende* or *blende*. The crystals belong to the isometric system and are interesting because they have almost the same atomic pattern as diamond (Fig. 1) and were the first to be studied with X-rays.

111

Though rarely met with in jewelry, cassiterite possesses all the attributes of a first-rate gem except hardness. Its optical characters rank close to the top—third in brilliancy and second in both color dispersion and birefringence. It is, incidentally, the heaviest of all the gems, surpassing even the opaque metallic stones in specific gravity.

Cassiterite, however, is valued chiefly for its content of tin. It is almost the only commercial source of the metal and is frequently called *tin-stone*. Its origin is in deposits formed by heated gases. Owing to its hardness, lack of cleavage, and resistance to chemical action, cassiterite is often concentrated in placers.

The localities in the Federated Malay States and the near-by Dutch islands of Sumatra, Banka, and Billiton have been brought to public attention by the war. Bolivia is the other main source of supply. The British deposits in Cornwall have been famous for 2,000 years. Australia, Mexico, East Africa, and central Europe are additional producers.

Crystals of cassiterite (Fig. 15) belong to the tetragonal system. They are sometimes twinned in an interesting knee shape. When sufficiently transparent for fashioning into gems, cassiterite is astonishingly beautiful. Combined with a diamondlike luster, the other optical properties provide rich overtones for the deep-golden color of the gem.

FLUORITE

The mineral fluorite formerly held its place in gemology as a compact violet and purple material called *blue-john*, much in demand for vases and other carved ornamental objects. Exhaustion of the noted deposits at Derbyshire in England turned attention to the beautiful faceted gems that can be cut from transparent fluorite. They may be almost any single color or in several multicolored combinations. Green and yellow tints are often considered the choicest. Rich green gems recently found in South-West Africa bear a reasonable resemblance to emerald. Attractive pink crystals come from Switzerland. Ontario, Canada, produces colorless ones. The United States is a major source of fluorite—lovely sea-green stones from the eastern deposits and purple stones from the extensive Kentucky-Illinois area and from Colorado.

Fluorite is composed of two chemical elements, calcium and fluorine. It may be referred to as a fluoride, or as a halide because fluorine belongs to the halogen group of elements, which also includes chlorine, bromine, and iodine. The root of its name, meaning "to flow," was originally applied to more than one fusible mineral, and was given also to the new element when the latter was discovered. The spectacular phenomenon of *fluorescence*, described in Chapter 8, was named because of the presence of this property in fluorite, although it is really the result of impurities in the stone. The massive material is popularly called *fluorspar*.

Fluorite belongs to the isometric system. Although it usually crystallizes in cubes, well shown in Fig. 72, its cleavage is octahedral and is so well developed that (with care) a perfect 8-sided octahedron can be broken from a typical 6-faced cube. Twinned crystals, grown together so that they penetrate each other, are common. Its easy cleavage and conspicuous lack of hardness make fluorite a difficult gem to cut or to wear.

113

In addition to furnishing specimens for faceting and carving, fluorite has a further gem use in the manufacture of imitation opal. Industrially, the common variety has

Fig. 72   Group of Cubic Fluorite Crystals
[Ward's Natural Science Establishment.]

great value as a flux in steel-making and as the source of hydrofluoric acid.

BRAZILIANITE

For the first time since the discovery of benitoite in 1907 an entirely new mineral species, not merely a new variety of a species already known, was added to the ranks of gems in 1945. Both the mineral and the gem were described from the same specimens in 1945 by Frederick H. Pough and Edward P. Henderson, who named them brazilianite in honor of the country in which they were found.

Brazilianite has a pleasing chartreuse-yellow color, like some chrysoberyl, and is transparent. Chemically, it is a hydrous phosphate of sodium and aluminum, more closely resembling turquoise in composition than other minerals, but physically it is a very different sort of material. Belonging to the monoclinic system, brazilianite has already been found in large crystals; and, although it is by no means abundant, it should become sufficiently accessible to gem lovers who appreciate its novelty as well as its beauty. Unfortunately, brazilianite is neither hard nor brilliant and must depend upon its color for any popular approval.

The best crystals and largest faceted gems may be seen in the American Museum of Natural History in New York and in the United States National Museum in Washington. They were taken from a pegmatite in a part of the state of Minas Geraes, Brazil, that is noted for its mica deposits.

APATITE

Although it is a fairly common mineral in many rocks, and crystals as large as several feet in length have been found, apatite is known only occasionally in gem quality. Its name bears no relation to food or digestion, but comes from the Greek word meaning "deceit"; there is a confusing similarity in appearance between apatite and other minerals because its varied colors resemble those of more-familiar gems. Some of these hues deserve wider recognition in themselves, however, for the pastel tints are truly lovely. *Asparagus-stone* is the popular and appropriate

115

name for the yellowish-green variety. Yellow apatite from Mexico has become better known in recent years. Violet, pink, blue, bluish-green, and green colors come from other countries. Maine, with its violet stones, is the chief American source.

Apatite is doubly refractive, as are all gems that crystallize in the hexagonal system, but hardly any other gem possesses the property of birefringence to a weaker degree. This has no practical effect on its beauty but is useful in identifying the stone on a refractometer. The inferior hardness of apatite is its really serious liability. It is the standard for number 5 in Mohs' scale and can be scratched even by a knife; hence it does not belong in a ring but is suitable for other types of jewelry.

Not only is apatite the most abundant mineral phosphate, deriving its essential element from widespread animal and plant remains, but it in turn furnishes the material for secondary phosphate gems such as turquoise.

SCAPOLITE

Best known in jewelry as *pink moonstone*, scapolite of gem quality is more common, however, in transparent pieces of other colors that make lovely faceted stones. These are rich golden in hue or decline to pale yellow and colorless. Faintly clouded specimens of pink, deep violet, and blue make most attractive moonstone and cat's-eye varieties.

The first gems were found in the ruby mines of Burma. Madagascar and Brazil supply most of the fine yellow stones, but those from South America seem at present to

116

be off the market. Colorless crystals are a product of the volcanic eruptions of Mount Vesuvius.

Scapolite designates a series of aluminum silicate minerals, in chemical composition very much like the feldspars with the addition of chloride, carbonate, and sulfate members. To make possible an easier classification the series has been divided arbitrarily into five parts which have been given specific names (the most familiar of which is *wernerite*), but they actually grade into one another. Scapolite belongs to the tetragonal system and has typical four-sided crystals of moderate hardness.

CORDIERITE

So intense is the dichroism of cordierite that the twin colors of the different rays of light passing through the gem can be seen without the aid of an instrument—deep blue when viewed down the length of the crystal, and pale blue or pale yellow when viewed across the width. Other commonly used but discredited names for this gem are "dichroite" (from its most characteristic property) and "iolite." "Water sapphire" is an improper name still used among the older jewelry firms and in Ceylon, the chief source.

Cordierite is about as hard and as heavy as quartz and, except for the extreme dichroism, resembles it in appearance; some of the violet stones, which look like amethyst, especially resemble quartz. Although cordierite belongs to the orthorhombic system, twinning causes many crystals to appear hexagonal; most of the gem material, however, occurs in rounded pebbles. Cordierite is a complex silicate of aluminum, iron, and magnesium. Its trans-

117

parency and hardness place it appropriately with the faceted gems, although specimens seem to be cut more often as cabochons.

ENSTATITE

Associated with diamond in the great mines of Kimberley are found several other gems of much less value but considerable interest. Perhaps the most beautiful of them is green enstatite. Having small orthorhombic prisms, the crystals furnish bright, transparent gems which would have a wider appeal if they were more numerous.

In spite of being called "green garnet," enstatite is in no way related to demantoid or any other garnet. It is a member of the important *pyroxene group* of minerals, which includes such gems as diopside, jadeite jade, and spodumene. Enstatite is a silicate of magnesium; it usually contains a variable amount of iron and may contain some aluminum. Iron and chromium together produce the best green color.

Although enstatite possesses only a moderate degree of hardness, its extreme resistance to heat and acids suggested its name, which is derived from the Greek word meaning "opponent." Besides South Africa, Burma also yields gem material. Meteorites, which are mineralogically similar to kimberlite, the diamond-bearing rock, furnish enstatite for the connoisseur.

As the amount of iron increases, enstatite darkens and grades first into *bronzite* and then next (at 15 per cent ferrous oxide) into *hypersthene*—the end member of this *enstatite series* of orthorhombic pyroxenes. Both of these minerals yield gems of a rather metallic appearance;

118

they are cut with rounded instead of faceted surfaces. Bronzite has a fibrous bronzy luster. Hypersthene exhibits a peculiar iridescence called *schiller*, caused by reflections from tiny brown scales of an unknown mineral enclosed within it.

DIOPSIDE

Attractive transparent gems of a bottle-green color are furnished by the mineral diopside. They resemble peridot but are less olive in shade. Diopside occurs in monoclinic crystals showing a good prism form and many faces. Its name comes from the Greek and means "double appearance" in reference to the property of double refraction, as a result of which each ray of light is split into two rays upon entering the stone (see Fig. 42).

Diopside is a silicate of calcium and magnesium belonging to the *pyroxene group* of minerals. The green color is due to iron; when chromium is present it gives a brighter tone. The hardness is fairly low for a gem.

Piedmont, Italy, supplies the most beautiful stones. From the Tirol province of Austria, the diamond mines of South Africa, and deposits on both the New York and Ontario sides of the St. Lawrence River come other fine gems. Brazil, Madagascar, and Ceylon are reported as recent sources. A fibrous cat's-eye variety comes from Burma.

The association of diopside with jadeite and feldspar is especially interesting in many of the "jade" objects of early man that have been found in Mexico and Central America, such as those shown in Figs. 88 and 89.

Violane is an Italian variety of diopside named for its excellent violet-blue color; because it is not transparent, it is cut as cabochons rather than faceted.

119

It is a long way from the world's largest crystal—90 tons of spodumene, 47 feet long, lying like a huge timber in the Etta Mine near Keystone, South Dakota—to the ex-

Fig. 73   Kunzite Crystals from Madagascar
[Ward's Natural Science Establishment.]

quisitely fragile gems of the same species which grace our dainty jewelry. Until the discovery in Brazil about 1870 of a transparent yellow variety suitable for gem purposes, spodumene was known only as an ordinary mineral, fairly common in pegmatites, from which it had been abstracted for use as the chief source of lithium, the lightest of all metals.

120

Since then, choice green and beautiful lilac gem varieties have also been found, and spodumene is now properly ranked with the significant gem minerals. The two special varieties just mentioned have their own names, hiddenite and kunzite; in gemology the name spodumene itself is generally applied only to the occasional bright yellow or yellowish-green gems from Brazil and Madagascar.

Spodumene—another of the *pyroxene group* of minerals —is a silicate of lithium and aluminum. Its monoclinic crystals (Fig. 73) are dominantly prismatic, marked parallel to their length by alternating grooves and ridges.

Hiddenite

The emerald-green variety of spodumene called hiddenite has been found only in one place, in Alexander County, North Carolina. Because of the descriptive origin of so many gem names, it might be guessed that this stone was named because its limited deposit was long concealed. It was actually named, however, in honor of William E. Hidden, who discovered in 1880 the original deposit from which some loose crystals had previously come, though their true composition was not learned until later. Gem lovers regret that no more new specimens of hiddenite are available.

Kunzite

Fascinating color changes make kunzite one of the loveliest of gems. It is perhaps the most difficult gem to cut because of the extreme perfection of the cleavage, but, when properly fashioned to take advantage of its extraor-

121

dinary dichroism, kunzite rewards us with gleams of lilac and pink exclusively its own. It was first found in 1902 at Pala, San Diego County, California, and named for George F. Kunz, Tiffany's gem expert. It has since been found in Connecticut, Maine, Massachusetts, Brazil, and Madagascar (Fig. 73).

BENITOITE

The story of benitoite is like a familiar chapter in astronomy in which a new star or planet is known to exist long before any observer can fairly claim to have seen it. In the identification of benitoite, the tale is even more involved. Before a single specimen was found, its crystal form was determined theoretically, and mathematics proved that such a rare class of crystals is possible in nature. When finally brought to light in 1907, it was not even recognized but was mistaken for sapphire. Only the curiosity of a California jeweler, Godfrey Eacret, led to further inquiry. He held a piece in front of a dichroscope and became doubtful of its identity when he saw twin colors of blue and white—a different combination from that which he expected. His suspicion was fully justified by the final disclosure that this rich blue stone of true sapphire color was not only a new gem but a completely new species of mineral, until then unknown to science. It was named in honor of San Benito County in which it was found. A wonderful group of crystals from this unique locality is shown in Fig. 74.

Not only does benitoite have such a strong dichroism that the separate colors are visible without an instrument, but the dispersion or fire is similarly remarkable, equalling diamond in strength. The spread of rainbow colors is less conspicuous in benitoite than in diamond, however, because it is masked by the bright blue of the gem itself.

Fig. 74   Large Benitoite Crystals from San Benito County, California

[Ward's Natural Science Establishment.]

Chemically, benitoite is a silicate of barium and titanium. Associated with it was another scarce titanium mineral called neptunite, previously found only in Greenland. In addition to the disadvantage of its rarity, benitoite is a little softer than the minute quartz particles that are ever present in the air.

123

The largest benitoite crystal weighs less than 8 carats and the others are considerably smaller. In fact, the largest cut stone in private ownership weighs only about one carat.

TOURMALINE

Among the fairest flowers of the gem universe is tourmaline. Its popularity grows yearly while gem collectors and jewelers vie with each other to obtain the finest specimens for their respective purposes. And with reason—for tourmaline is one of the wonders of the mineral kingdom, presenting an incomparable diversity of color, a complex crystal form, a remarkable range of physical properties, a curious history. That it was known to the ancients is shown by references in their writings to certain of its distinctive characteristics; but its exact nature was not understood and it was thoroughly confused with other gems, and its individuality was lost during the unscientific ages that followed. In the middle of the 17th century some long crystals of a dark-green color reached Europe from Brazil and were called "Brazilian emerald," a name which has since been applied commonly (though of course incorrectly) to all green tourmaline.

One summer day in 1703, in the city of Amsterdam, the story was further complicated. Several children were playing in a courtyard with some colored stones which had been brought, together with other foreign merchandise, from distant Ceylon, then a Dutch possession. The hot sun shone down unmercifully, and under its influence the stones lost their passiveness and began to attract and repel light objects such as ashes and straws. The perplexed traders were unable to account for this startling

124

evidence of animation, and disposed of the matter by naming the strange playthings *aschentrekkers* or "ash-drawers." The story spread abroad and the French Academy of Sciences was presented with a demonstration of the mineral's inexplicable powers.

For a period of about forty years serious investigation ceased, but interest was suddenly revived when a German physician published the results of his private research on the subject. Philosophers throughout Europe joined with physicists in discussing the mystery, and fashionable society listened with eager curiosity. Specimens were rare —a Dr. Heberden had the only one in England—so that it was not until other crystals could be obtained that their similarity to certain black stones which had been known for many years was discovered. For them all the name tourmaline, derived from an old Singhalese word, was adopted. Each color variety has its own name, a relic of the time when their common relationship was unsuspected.

The major part of American tourmaline has been found in the two most widely separated states, Maine and California, as though Nature wanted to grace both shores of the continent with the gem which, above all others, reflects the ever-varying hues of sea and land. Indians and cowboys collected tourmaline in California as early as 1872, and the deposits in San Diego and Riverside Counties were perhaps the choicest in the world, especially notable for the size and the perfection of their crystals. Pink stones have been shipped rather extensively to China (the trade amounting to $100,000 in the peak year), where many of the stones have been cut and resold as finished gems or ornaments.

Tourmaline was discovered in the State of Maine quite by accident. One day at the close of autumn in 1820 two students, Elijah Hamlin and Ezekiel Holmes, stopped on the summit of a grassy knoll to admire the sunset, when one of them was attracted by a flash of green light which caught the corner of his eye. Turning to the place he saw a broken piece of a green mineral crystal lying among the earthy roots of a tree upturned by the wind. Search for additional specimens was prevented by approaching darkness, and plans were laid for the next day. But during the night winter came with a heavy snow which covered the ground until spring. On the first clear day of the following year the two young men resumed their explorations, and from cavities in the rock weakened by the elements they brought to view some beautiful crystals—clear, bright, richly colored, delicately formed. They were the first of the splendid tourmalines which were to astound gem collectors during the following decades. From there—Mount Mica in the town of Paris—and from Hebron and Auburn within close range, have come some thousands of excellent stones.

A few tourmalines have been found in other states also, especially Connecticut. They occur in many countries but only a limited number are important producers. Brazilian stones are widely known and admired and constitute a leading mineral resource of that nation. Superb gems have come from Russia and Siberia. Elba, the island to which Napoleon was exiled after Leipzig, has yielded a variety of colors. Madagascar tourmalines are equal in beauty to those found in more accessible places, and Burma, Ceylon, India, and Africa are additional sources of good-quality material.

Color—this one word describes the tremendous appeal which tourmaline has for the discriminating lover of gems.

Color in single hues and in polychrome, color exquisitely blended and sharply contrasted, color richly streaked and delicately modulated, color usually serene, sometimes glowing, often shy and furtive—evanescent tints which come into view and as quickly disappear or merge into others. For tourmaline is characterized by a pronounced dichroism, so strong that the individual components of the color may be seen without an instrument as the gem is turned. John Ruskin says whimsically in *Ethics of the Dust*, "All the light that gets into it, I believe, comes out a good deal the worse, and is not itself again for a long while." Expert cutting endeavors to obtain the most favorable color from each crystal.

Tourmaline varies from water-clear and colorless to opaque and black and includes practically every known shade and tint of the spectrum's hues. A single crystal may be half-red and half-green, crowned with white, with lines of demarcation so sharp that the parts seem to have been cemented together. Or one of those from Elba may be colorless for its entire length except a black top; or a prism from Madagascar may have a whole row of different colors along its edge. Rare specimens have blue and green at extreme ends. Many crystals are zoned in the opposite way, so that a piece cut as a loaf of bread is sliced shows a somewhat circular center of one color surrounded by rings of other colors. Brazilian stones often have a red core encircled by a white zone and a green outer border, resembling a round slice of watermelon. Many California crystals are similar but have the succession of colors reversed. This color arrangement of tourmaline is perhaps the most remarkable feature of a mineral replete with wonder.

127

Rose and pink tourmaline is called *rubellite*. Fine gems command a high price, particularly those approaching ruby in depth of color. "Brazilian sapphire" is blue tourmaline, and *indicolite* is a deeper blue. "Brazilian emerald" is green tourmaline, which is relatively widespread in Brazil; a few gems from South Africa are a color that rivals emerald and are distinguished from it partly by their superior brilliancy. "Ceylonese peridot" is honey-yellow tourmaline, and "Brazilian peridot" is yellowish-green tourmaline. Of the other varieties, *siberite* is violet, *dravite* is brown, and *schorl* is black; colorless tourmaline is called *achroite*. As mentioned before, these colors occur in almost any combination, so that tourmaline has earned for itself the sobriquet, "the rainbow gem." *Tourmaline cat's-eye* is sufficiently fibrous to show a wavy band of light when the stone is cut with a rounded top.

Crystals of tourmaline are unique among minerals. They are the only ones that occur in prisms having a rounded triangular outline, and they are always lined and furrowed along their length. See Figs. 19, 75, and 76. When the crystals have faces developed at both terminations, the forms at the two ends are different. This phenomenon is known as *polarity* and is made evident in various other ways. When a crystal of tourmaline is either heated or cooled it is electrically charged, positive at one end and negative at the opposite, attracting and repelling small particles, as was noticed by the Dutch children two and one-half centuries ago.

The chemical composition of tourmaline is extremely complex. To quote Ruskin again, in answer to Mary's question, "And what is it made of?"—"A little of every-

128

Fig. 75   Group of Tourmaline Crystals
from New York

[Elmer B. Rowley.]

Fig. 76   Gem Tourmaline Crystal from Brazil
[Ward's Natural Science Establishment.]

thing; there's always flint, and clay, and magnesia in it; and the black is iron, according to its fancy; and there's boracic acid, if you know what it is; and if you don't, I cannot tell you today, and it doesn't signify; and there's potash and soda; and, on the whole, the chemistry of it is more like a medieval doctor's prescription than the making of a respectable mineral." The different kinds of tourmaline really belong to a mineral series. The beautiful tints are due mostly to the presence of alkalies. Rubellite owes its lovely red to lithium and, associated with the lithium mica, lepidolite, forms attractive museum specimens. Brown tourmaline contains magnesium, and the black stones are, as Ruskin said, colored by iron.

Tourmaline is suitable for all types of jewelry, but its moderate hardness and its wealth of pleasing color render it especially desirable for costuming. Black tourmaline has had a limited vogue as a mourning stone. Besides its ornamental uses, for which its color is responsible, tourmaline has a number of scientific applications that are due to its peculiar electrical properties. It measures the intensity of radium emanations; in "tourmaline tongs" it serves to detect polarization; small variations in pressure, such as those experienced by submarines, are registered by it; and it is valued for experimental work in electricity. During World War II it proved to be the only substance that could measure the pressure developed by the explosion of nuclear bombs.

Because of its exceptional color characteristics and its intriguing story, tourmaline has been successfully featured by many jewelers, who have used it to create a new fashion among the gem-loving American public. Collectors of beautiful things display their pieces of tourmaline with justifiable pride.

Beryl is a mineral species comprising several gem varieties the names of which are more familiar than its own. The only gems, in fact, sold simply as beryl are those of a pale green color. The rest have distinctive popular names —emerald, aquamarine, morganite, heliodor, and goshenite. The first two, emerald and aquamarine, deserve special attention, for they are among the choicest precious stones.

The mineral beryl is a silicate of aluminum and beryllium (a chemical element named for it). Small amounts of other elements replace these and are responsible for the individual colors that so glorify the jeweler's window. Without coloring matter, irregular masses of beryl are white; many of them probably are mistaken every day for common quartz. Crystallized beryl without coloring matter is clear and transparent, hardly different in appearance from glass except for its hexagonal outline; occasionally it is called *goshenite*.

Crystals of beryl have a characteristic shape, prisms with six sides. Usually the ends are flat, though sometimes they are modified by small faces which give a tapering effect, as shown in Fig. 18. Huge crystals of beryl, weighing hundreds of pounds but of no use for gem purposes, occur in some deposits. Such specimens (and smaller ones as well) have acquired a vital place in modern industry, because the metal beryllium taken from them makes a copper alloy which has a tensile strength far greater than that of

131

any known steel and can be made into springs that will actually flex billions of times before wearing out.

Emerald

Of all the gems that might have been chosen as the birthstone for May, none could be more appropriate than emerald, "green as a meadow in spring." A fine emerald, completely transparent and of an intense velvety color will bring a truly astonishing price; such a stone may well be called the rarest of gems.

Deficient in brilliancy and fire, even somewhat in durability, emerald depends for its popularity entirely upon its unsurpassed color. (Chromium oxide is the coloring agent.) Freedom from flaws is much less important than color unless the structure is quite poor; flaws, in fact, are often reproduced in imitation emeralds.

The first emeralds came from mines known to Alexander the Great. These deposits were rediscovered in the Egyptian desert near the Red Sea by an expedition sent out in 1818 to search for the ancient diggings which had been lost for so long that their existence seemed mythical. Cleopatra was one of the best customers of these mines and gave many of the stones to her favorite ambassadors. Caesar collected emeralds, presumably for their supposed curative value. Specimens have been found in mummy wrappings, in Etruscan tombs, and in the ruins excavated at Pompeii and Herculaneum. Charlemagne's crown and the famous Iron Cross of Lombardy were both set with emeralds. When Henry II was made king of Ireland in 1171 he is said to have been given an emerald ring as symbol of his authority; if the story is true, this is a pertinent association between the gem and the Emerald Isle.

The Crusaders and Marco Polo returned from the Orient with emeralds among their treasures. But these excited little interest compared with the amazement expressed when the Conquistadores returned to Spain with vast quantities of emeralds of a larger size and a more beautiful color than had ever been seen before. These "Spanish" or "Peruvian" emeralds, which actually had come from Colombia, were seized from their owners, the Incas, who worshiped some of them and guarded them in sacred temples. Preferring the destruction of their beloved green gems to their theft, the priests told the conquerors that real emeralds could not be broken, and a goodly number of stones were thus sacrificed in attempts to prove their genuineness. Deliberately hidden from white men, some of the mines were later found accidentally; others may yet remain undisclosed. The densely jungled elevations of Colombia still produce the world's finest emeralds, so gently described by O. O. McIntyre as "like wet grass in the shadow of great trees after a summer rain." Muzo, Chivor, and Coscuez have furnished most of the crystals for several decades. For various reasons, some economic but others political and rather fantastic, these mines have been worked only sporadically.

So characteristic is the parallel, steplike pattern of cutting that is used for this gem that the name *emerald cut* has been given to it. Many expensive diamonds also are fashioned in emerald cut; conversely some emeralds are cut in the usual *brilliant* style of diamond.

Emerald is more easily fractured than the other varieties

133

of beryl and is slightly (though not to any important extent) less hard than the rest.

Very recently emerald has been added to the limited number of gems made synthetically on a commercial basis. Other man-made substitutes for emerald are either solid glass or composite stones assembled from two or three pieces of various materials. All of these are explained in Chapter 7.

In addition to the gems from Colombia, choice small emeralds have come from the Siberian side of the Ural Mountains. Brazil, the Tirol, the Transvaal, and North Carolina are other sources, but they seldom figure in the market.

Aquamarine

The pleasant name aquamarine comes from the Latin words for "sea water," so descriptive of its color, a lovely blend of blue and green, varying like the color of the sea itself. Most of the stones are greenish blue to bluish green, one hue or the other predominating, though some are pure blue. Occasionally yellowish-green beryl has been called aquamarine, but the newer name of *chrysolite aquamarine* seems preferable. Iron oxide is the coloring agent in all aquamarines.

Aquamarine's popularity during recent years is a continuation from the time when it was the only gem regularly faceted by the Romans, who valued it for eardrops and unengraved ring stones. It was one of the favorite engraving stones of European Renaissance artists. From it the people of India have cut long cylindrical beads to be strung on elephant hair. Flattering to blonde and brunette alike, aquamarine harmonizes with fabric of every color, and it is one of the few stones which retains its full beauty under artificial light.

Since ancient times aquamarine has symbolized happiness and everlasting youth, perhaps because of its purity

Fig. 77   Mount Antero, Colorado

Noted source of aquamarine, and the highest gem locality (14,245 feet) in North America. [H. L. Standley.]

of color and the remarkable absence of flaws in its structure. Stories have been told that some persons who wear aquamarine rings are able to forecast the weather by the changing tint of the stone; but this feature, however interesting, seems to have no scientific foundation.

Aquamarine is one of the many gems found in pegmatites. Brazil, the most prolific of all the gem-producing nations, long has been the chief source of aquamarine crystals, some of which are very large. Deep-blue stones

135

bring high prices, owing to the prosperous expansion of the entire world's gem and lapidary industry since the Second World War. The bare and hilly state of Minas Geraes is the main producing district of most of the kinds of gems, and most of the cutting is done in three towns.

Siberia, Ceylon, and Madagascar are other leading producers. Not many American aquamarines reach the market at present, but California, Maine, Connecticut, and North Carolina have supplied more than a few choice gems. The highest mineral locality in North America is an aquamarine deposit on the rugged slopes of Mount Antero, Colorado, at an altitude of over 14,000 feet. Fig. 77 is a view of this great mountain

Morganite

The financial encouragement given by J. Pierpont Morgan to the study and the collecting of gems caused the pink and rose variety of beryl, first produced in 1902, to be named in his honor. The Morgan collection in the American Museum of Natural History in New York is one of the best in the world.

Colored by the element lithium, morganite varies from pale pink to salmon to a rich rose red. It occurs with other pink minerals. The gem-laden island of Madagascar in the Indian Ocean off the east coast of Africa is the main source of the most beautiful morganite. Deposits in San Diego County, California, have yielded numerous crystals of a less desirable salmon hue. Brazilian morganite is generally pale.

136

Heliodor

Yellow beryl has been known in Ceylon for centuries, but the discovery in South-West Africa in 1910 of a magnificent golden stone of the same species aroused a new interest in beryl of this color. It was named heliodor, meaning "gift of the sun." In addition to the iron oxide that causes the color of regular yellow beryl, heliodor contains a radioactive substance that intensifies its splendor. Besides Africa, good localities for heliodor and yellow beryl are Ceylon and the Soviet Union, and especially the Brazilian state of Minas Geraes.

DANBURITE

First found at Danbury in Connecticut, danburite is the only gem species other than benitoite to bear the name of an American mineral locality. Danburite is related to topaz in chemical composition and crystal form, and it resembles yellow topaz in color. Madagascar produces deep-yellow gemmy danburite; other stones descending through various degrees of yellow to completely colorless ones are said to come from there and also from Burma and Japan.

Danburite is a silicate of boron and calcium. Its orthorhombic crystals have much the same prismatic shape as topaz but are not handicapped by the latter's fragile cleavage. A luster of more than average brightness, a good refractive power and consequently an adequate brilliancy when cut, and a hardness equal to quartz make danburite a worth-while gem mineral.

When Job praised the value of wisdom and said, "The topaz of Ethiopia shall not equal it," he referred to a stone which we know today as *peridot*, the gem variety of the mineral olivine. Its source was an ancient mystery, as the older name may indicate, since the word topaz may perhaps be derived from the name of the island Topazios in the Red Sea where the gem was obtained. According to the story, the place was thus named because it was so hidden by fogs that mariners had difficulty in locating it. This triangle-shaped island, now called Zeberged or St. John's, is 34 miles off the coast of Egypt. Pirates are said to have been the first to land there and to have discovered the stones in crevices in the rock. Knowledge of the place was later lost to the outside world for centuries. Almost the entire supply of peridot has come from this one locality. Many fine stones were brought to Europe by the Crusaders who thought them emeralds, and a large number of the peridots sold today have been recut from these historic gems. The new supply is limited; some crystals that appeared in the American market not long ago were purchased avidly.

At its finest, peridot has a rich bottle-green shade different from any other gem. So lovely is this stone that it often has been called "evening emerald." A more modern description comes from a French journalist: "Peridot is primeval green, green as a signal light." Its name frequently is pronounced in the original French way, to rhyme with "go," as well as in the Anglicized way to rhyme with "got."

138

Olivine received its name from its typical olive-green color and its olive-oil luster. *Chrysolite*, meaning "golden stone," is the attractive name properly given by jewelers to the variety of olivine that has a yellow or greenish-yellow color, but this term is so generally misused in reference to other gems that are blends of green and yellow that it has almost lost its individuality. Furthermore, chrysolite is a mineral name accepted as a synonym of the species olivine and the *olivine series* (forsterite to fayalite).

No gem could have a more amazing career than the olivine found in meteorites—strange celestial visitors, the only things from outside his own Earth that man is able to see and touch and analyze. Peridot of a size and quality actually suitable for use in jewelry is a constituent of the solid part of some of these "shooting stars."

In addition to the Egyptian island already mentioned as the chief source of peridot, other places from which gem material comes are the diamond mines of South Africa, and localities in Ceylon, Brazil, Burma, Australia, and the United States. In the Navajo land of Arizona and New Mexico large rounded pebbles of peridot have been eroded from the primary rock to find their way into ant hills and sand dunes.

Chemically, olivine is a silicate of magnesium and iron, which replace each other in varying proportions. In hardness it is inferior to the majority of the well-known gems and thus is better adapted to pins and necklaces than rings. Crystals of olivine, though often much abraded, usually show the stubby prism of the orthorhombic system to which they belong (see Fig. 21).

139

More phenakite has been found than the scarcity of cut gems might indicate. Owing to the interesting forms displayed by the hexagonal crystals, most of them are doubtless left in their original state without being fashioned.

The name (formerly also spelled "phenacite") is derived from the Greek word meaning "deceiver" because of the frequency with which the crystals have been mistaken for quartz. The superior optical properties of phenakite, however, make identification certain when instruments are used.

Phenakite is usually colorless but may be light brown, bright yellow, or rose. Some phenakite is very transparent and, although somewhat lacking in fire, has an exceptionally appealing luster.

A silicate of the rare element beryllium, phenakite occurs with other gems, especially beryl, that are chemically related. Mount Antero, Colorado, is the most important locality in North America. Here aquamarine, the gem variety of beryl, has been partly dissolved, furnishing beryllium for the subsequent growth of the phenakite. Beautiful large crystals have come from the emerald mines of the Ural Mountains, a gold mine in Brazil, and Tanganyika in East Africa.

WILLEMITE

Occasional clear slender prisms of willemite, of a delicate apple-green color, and a few transparent light-yellow pieces as well, have been cut into gems. Willemite belongs to the hexagonal system of crystallization. It is fairly heavy but not very hard. Its most startling property is a bright fluorescence, described in Chapter 8. Only from the great zinc mines of the Franklin-Sterling Hill district of Sussex County, New Jersey, has come gem-quality material, though ordinary willemite is found in a few other places.

Willemite is a silicate of zinc, constituting in New Jersey an important ore of that metal. Intensified production during the war diverted to industrial use many specimens that might otherwise have gone into collections. The Franklin area is noted for its tremendous variety of minerals, many of which do not occur anywhere else in the world. Willemite is intimately associated with franklinite and zincite, the three minerals together forming handsome multicolored specimens.

GARNET

Garnet represents more than merely a single mineral having several color varieties. It is really a group of minerals, comprising half a dozen subspecies, five of which have gem varieties of their own. The chemical formula is uniform in type for all the garnets, and the constituent elements are interchangeable when their atoms are approximately equal in size, though the total valence or combining power must be maintained. This ability of atoms or ions to replace one another, called *isomorphism*, explains the range in composition and the variation in properties. Some kinds of garnet, however, like some cousins among the human race, do not mix as freely as others; and even among the more hybrid garnets there is usually a sharp enough distinction to enable a proper classification to be

141

made. Gem garnets especially may be properly classified since, like all gems, they are more exclusive, more restricted in their range, than common minerals.

Few other gems are as widely sold as garnet, but few are so misunderstood. Garnet has been sold under a host of

Fig. 78 Garnet Crystal in Pegmatite from Pennsylvania
[From Hawkins *The Book of Minerals*, copyright 1935.]

false names, though even the correct names are confusing, particularly to those persons who, familiar only with the reddish-brown stones, do not know that garnet occurs in almost every color except blue. Many of the lesser-known garnets are certainly attractive and some are highly valuable.

Garnet crystals (Figs. 12 and 78) may be easily recognized by their distinctive shape, usually having either 12 or 24 faces, each 4- or 6-sided, unless they are worn by the

142

processes of nature to nearly round pebbles. Although most of them are small, some attain fairly large sizes; one crystal weighing over nine pounds was found in 1885 in an excavation just off Broadway in New York City. Lacking cleavage, garnet is not easily broken. Because of its high refractive index it is very brilliant when properly cut.

Ordinary garnet, of no gem value, is used as an industrial abrasive for polishing wood and leather. During the war a nonskid, fireproof, plastic material containing particles of garnet went into service on battleship decks to prevent accidents caused by slipping.

Synthetic garnet is not made commercially; on the contrary, the real stone is substituted for more expensive ones in composite man-made gems to give them a hard outer surface.

Modern research has shown the existence within the garnet group of two natural isomorphous series, each named for the subspecies that constitutes its middle member. One—called the *almandite series*—embraces pyrope, almandite, and spessartite. The other—the *andradite series*—includes grossularite, andradite, and uvarovite. Each of these subspecies except uvarovite (which yields no gems) is described in this section.

Pyrope

Pyrope, the best-known garnet used in jewelry, is a silicate of magnesium and aluminum. Its name is derived from the Greek word meaning "fiery," because of its sparklike color, red with a yellowish cast.

Properly known as *Bohemian garnet* from its former chief place of origin, this stone is frequently sold as a variety of ruby under such fraudulent names as "Cape ruby," "Arizona ruby," and "Colorado ruby." In each instance the adjective discloses the source.

A virtual flood of pyrope garnets came from Bohemia in the 19th century. They were mounted in pins and brooches of unattractive Victorian design, and their abundance gave them (and all garnets) an unpleasant reputation among women of fashion. Even the discovery of really beautiful pyrope in the diamond mines of South Africa failed to restore its popularity, and misleading names were adopted for merchandising purposes. Pyrope is found in lesser amounts in other countries besides those mentioned, and in Colorado, Arizona, New Mexico, and Utah in the United States.

Rhodolite

The exquisite color of roses and rhododendrons is preserved forever in the rare rhodolite garnet. In composition it stands between pyrope and almandite, consisting of two parts of the former mineral to one part of the latter. In addition to its well-known occurrence in Macon County, western North Carolina, where it was first reported in 1893, rhodolite comes also from the gem gravels of Ceylon. Most of the crystals are tiny, and consequently the cut gems are even smaller, but their lovely color is a delight to any eye fortunate enough to see them.

Almandite

As the magnesium is replaced by ferric iron, pyrope grades imperceptibly into almandite. Roman gem engrav-

144

ers were fond of this garnet, known popularly as *alman-dine* but preferably as *almandite*, and from it they carved some superb cameos and intaglios. The Head of the Dog Sirius in the Marlborough collection is considered the finest intaglio ever created. A portrait of Plato engraved in almandite is the most familiar likeness of him.

At its best this garnet has a deep, clear red color, usually tinged with violet. It is highly prized in India, where the wealthy classes call it *precious garnet* and wear it with their diamonds and rubies. Almandite is the gem known for 2,000 years as *carbuncle*, and it has often been cut with a rounded top. This style of cutting (*cabochon*) is itself at times wrongly called carbuncle, but the latter word should be applied only to a red garnet so fashioned. The mineralogical spelling *almandite* is a scientific approach to uniform terminology.

That amazing optical instrument, the spectroscope (Fig. 47), which reveals the intimate secrets of chemistry, shows a typical iron absorption spectrum in almandite, especially in the violet stones.

Almandite gems come from the prolific deposits of Ceylon, from India, from Brazil and Uruguay in South America, and from a few other countries. Stones suitable for jewelry are found in about a dozen states of the United States but are hardly numerous. The large garnet crystal previously mentioned which was uncovered in New York City was almandite. The interesting crystals from Alaska have almost no value as gems. Almandite is the garnet most widely used as an abrasive; some commercial deposits, such as the one near Lake George, New York, also contain gem material.

Spessartite

One of the prettiest of the garnets is unfortunately too rare, and usually too small, to attract much notice. Spessartite, the manganese-aluminum garnet, is usually red of a golden or brownish hue. The mineral is fairly common in Maine and elsewhere in the United States, but gem-quality material comes from only a few localities. Tiny perfect crystals are found in cavities in three volcanic hills at Nathrop, Colorado. A number of good stones have come from northern Brazil. Other scattered sources include Ceylon, Burma, and Australia. The locality of Spessart in Bavaria gave its name to spessartite or *spessartine*.

Grossularite

Garnets with a hazy, spotted interior that indicates a granular structure belong to the subspecies known as grossularite, the calcium-aluminum member of the group. Stones the color of gooseberries give the mineral its name, from the Latin word for that berry. When they have the golden-brown color of cinnamon they are called *hessonite* or *cinnamon-stone*. Even choicer colors are orange, called *hyacinth-garnet*, and reddish brown, called *jacinth-garnet*. Translucent bright-green grossularite has been discovered in South Africa and is sold as "Transvaal jade"—which it would probably resemble if there were any jade in the Transvaal! A pink variety of grossularite in snow-white marble is mined in Mexico. The other colors come mainly from Ceylon. *Grossular* is another name.

Andradite

The most remarkable of all the garnets is green. Its name is *demantoid*, which means "diamond-like," and it is a variety of the mineral andradite. Here is a gem with a flashing luster, a fiery inner brilliancy, and the most extreme display of rainbow colors shown by any major precious stone. Although it may give forth yellowish tints, its choicest hue is a true emerald green. Demantoid was discovered in the Ural Mountains during the middle of the past century. At first it was believed to be emerald and was called "Uralian emerald"; now it is sometimes sold also as "olivine"; both names are erroneous and are used merely because they are supposed to sound more attractive. This wonderful rare gem needs no such deception. Inasmuch as it is found only in small sizes and is not especially hard, it is usually limited to being a foil for other, larger stones. Many have been set in rows and circles in diamond-set rings and sold as emeralds.

Two other gem varieties of andradite are known. *Topazolite*, named for its resemblance to yellow topaz, has come from Switzerland and Italy. *Melanite* is black and has served in mourning jewelry.

All three kinds of andradite are calcium-iron garnets and are the softest of the entire garnet group.

EPIDOTE

The pistachio color of epidote is easily recognized. Faceted gems have been cut from transparent crystals of this distinctive yellowish-green shade and have often been

147

called *pistacite*. Other clear hues exist, but they are not so well known, although opaque green specimens are very common in metamorphic rocks.

Epidote is the general name given to a group of important minerals, as well as to a series within the group and specifically to the most abundant member. They are hydrous silicates of calcium, aluminum, iron, and other elements. Another mineral in the group, zoisite, is described in the chapter on "Cabochon and Carved Gems." Epidote itself is monoclinic, and its crystals are often handsome, having a prismatic aspect and exhibiting many faces. Gem material has come from Austria, Italy, and Norway.

ZIRCON

Zircon is no longer the gem of mystery. Until the last few years, however, less had been known about its constitution than about that of any other precious stone, and its history, even the origin of its name, is still obscure. Yet zircon is one of the oldest gems; its scientific nature makes it one of the most extraordinary.

Early in the 20th century three kinds of zircon, rather than one, were believed to exist. To avoid the confusion of giving them separate names, it has been more convenient to refer to them as high, low, and intermediate zircon, according to the physical and optical properties.

According to this interpretation *high zircon* is the fully crystallized silicate of the element zirconium. *Low zircon* has no outward crystal form and is apparently a mixture of amorphous oxide of silicon and some kind of zirconium oxide, which may be partly crystalline. *Intermediate zircon* is composed of both the normal silicate and the separate

148

oxides and fills the gap between the extreme high and low types.

The current decade has revealed more intimately the physical secrets of zircon and showed that the so-called

Fig. 79   Zircon Crystals in Matrix
[Ward's Natural Science Establishment.]

high zircon is the normal kind and includes most of the gem varieties. High zircon belongs to the tetragonal system and occurs in square prisms with pyramids at both ends (Figs. 14 and 79). A twin crystal is shown in Fig. 3. Radioactivity due to the presence of thorium breaks down the crystalline structure to an increasing extent until, by a gradual transition accompanied by changes in specific gravity, refractive index, and other properties, the mineral becomes low zircon. The cloudiness characteristic of many zircons is evidence of their internal disintegration from the normal state.

With these variations in structure is a similar variation in color. Perhaps zircon has no such complete extent of hues as is found in corundum or tourmaline. But there is enough choice to satisfy most tastes, and some of the colors are indeed splendid. The deep-red gems reflect from their depths a penetrating glow, and the green stones with their peaceful beauty present a fine contrast. The rich golden-yellow gems are truly magnificent, surpassing all other stones of that color. The lovely blue zircons are deservedly popular, having been named *starlite* by Dr. Kunz because of their resemblance to "stars twinkling in the night." By no means least in interest are the colorless gems, whose resplendent brilliancy, dazzling luster, and concentrated fire make them the nearest rival of diamonds. Normal zircon is most likely to range from colorless to orange red or blue. Altered zircon may be brown, yellow, or green.

Zircon was better known until recently by the names of its varieties, *hyacinth* and *jacinth*, which appear in the older literature. The word zircon, which may have been derived from an Arabian or Persian word that described one of the colors of the stone, was rarely used in the gem trade until the introduction of the blue and the colorless kinds, but it has now become thoroughly familiar. It has largely superseded the names starlite for the blue, and *jargoon* or "Matura diamond" for the colorless zircon. The word Matura is similar to Matara, the southernmost harbor of Ceylon, from where the transparent colorless gem was exported.

Both *hyacinth* and *jacinth* are now correctly applied to red, orange, yellow, and brown zircons of gem quality, although if a distinction is made, hyacinth may be the reddish brown and jacinth the more nearly pure orange in color. Surely the best improvement would be to call all of them zircon, with suitable adjectives to indicate the color.

Ancient artists found zircon a responsive medium for their skill. Greek gem carvers specialized in intaglios, in which the design was incised below the surface; the Romans engraved both intaglios and cameos, most of the latter being in the darker stones. These classic specimens are characterized by roundness of line and shallowness of figure to avoid cracking the gem. Renaissance artists worked much with pale-yellow zircon, but produced cameos slightly inferior to the best of earlier periods.

The feature of zircon marketing that has attracted the greatest interest is the artificial production of certain colors. When the starlite blue, the golden-yellow, and the colorless diamondlike varieties began to acquire extensive popularity in America after the First World War, considerable discussion was aroused about their occurrence in nature. Some of them have indeed been found, but only rarely, and a profitable industry was built up at that time in the creation of these desirable colors. The Oriental process that is used has become generally known only since 1936. Between 850 and 1,000 degrees centigrade the reddish-brown stones from Indo-China usually turn golden yellow or colorless when heated in air, and blue or colorless when heated in the absence of air. Nothing dishonest is involved in this method of changing the color; the other properties remain about the same, and the chief effect is to give us gems that are admittedly more beautiful.

Most of the heat treating, as well as the cutting, is done across the border from Indo-China at Bangkok, the capital of Siam; some zircon is also found in that country. Burma is another source. The brown, yellow, and green gems from Ceylon continued to be available even during the Japanese conquest of southeastern Asia.

The gem district of Ceylon lies between Kandy, the capital, and the south shore near Ratnapura, which means "City of Gems" in Singhalese. In this interesting oriental island, known to the Chinese as the "Isle of Gems," is the greatest concentration of precious stones in the world, the deposits furnishing every important species with the single exception of diamond. The stones are scattered throughout a layer of gravel called *illam*, which lies under a thick bed of clay. Above the clay is fertile ground cultivated for centuries as rice fields. The work is done by natives who receive three-fifths of the proceeds. A pit is dug and the earth is hauled to the surface in baskets; then it is washed in a stream, and the stones are separated from the mud. They are sorted into groups according to size and quality. Many crystals have been worn into irregularly rounded pebbles by the sorting action of running water, which, together with tropical conditions of weathering, aggregates the gems into placer deposits.

Some fine zircon has been taken from places outside the Orient. Yellowish-red stones come from Russia, and red gems of good color have been found in New South Wales. The diamond-bearing rock at Kimberley in South Africa carries a quantity of yellowish-brown crystals of zircon, which are called by the miners "Dutch bort," a disreputable epithet justified by their lack of value. Zircon occurs at several localities in the United States, but material suitable for fashioning into gems is rarely encountered. The clear and brilliant crystals from the Pikes Peak region of Colorado are unfortunately too small.

That zircon has other remarkable qualities besides color to make it a most worth-while citizen of the gem kingdom is evident from a brief mention of its physical properties. A happy combination of an adamantine luster, a high refractive index, and a dispersion only 14 per cent lower than that of diamond makes a fine colorless zircon resemble a diamond so closely that in direct sunlight or under bright artificial illumination not many persons can easily discriminate between them.

Zircon is not characterized by excessive hardness and is peculiarly subject to chipping around its edges; yet if given the careful treatment due all rare and valuable things, zircon will reward its owner with long and faithful service, giving constantly what it most possesses—beauty.

The specific gravity is higher than that of any other major nonmetallic gemstone, so that a zircon is smaller in diameter than a diamond of the same weight.

In the history of chemistry zircon is noted for having furnished to science two rather rare elements. Zirconium was discovered in the mineral in 1789 and named after it, and the most closely related element, hafnium, was first detected in a Norwegian zircon in 1922.

Datolite leads a double life. European writers refer to the pale-green and yellow gems cut from transparent crystals of complex forms. Americans, on the other hand, are better acquainted with the light-colored, often mottled, opaque masses resembling unglazed porcelain which are found with inclusions of native copper in the Lake Superior copper district of Michigan. The facet-cut type is the more valuable because it is rarer and more difficult to cut, and therefore deserves primary consideration.

Datolite is a silicate of boron and calcium, which crystallizes in the monoclinic system and has an inferior degree of hardness. Its curious crystals are found in the United States in New Jersey, Massachusetts, and Connecticut, and in central Europe, especially Austria.

Very similar in chemical composition to danburite, which is sometimes found with it, datolite is closely related in a structural way to euclase (which may be said to belong to the *datolite family*). None of these three gems has more than a limited use.

EUCLASE

Like aquamarine, euclase is a gem containing the element beryllium (as a hydrous silicate of beryllium and aluminum), and also, like aquamarine, it comes in delicately lovely tints of blue and green. The chief reason, apart from a certain rarity, why stones cut from euclase are infrequently seen is their very perfect cleavage, which makes cutting difficult. The name of the mineral, in fact, means "good cleavage." Its resistance to scratching is almost equal to that of aquamarine. Euclase occurs in prismatic crystals of the monoclinic system. Gem-quality stones come from Brazil, the Ural Mountains, India, and East Africa.

TOPAZ

Topaz recommends itself to the aesthetic taste by its perfect transparency, its velvety luster, its enchanting hues, and its softly diffused body appearance. Topaz is indeed an appropriate birthstone for November, mirroring the golden tone of autumn leaves and the rich glow of Indian-summer sunsets. Yet all topaz is not yellow, nor are all yellow stones topaz, as is widely believed. The colors of topaz are many; they are usually of delicate tint; there are few dark stones. Red colors are especially scarce, but clever applications of heat, called "pinking" and carried on mostly in Brazil, turns some brownish topaz to the blushing rose and pink hues that have been in vogue during recent years. Blue and light-green topaz are indeed lovely. Even the colorless stones are appealing, for there is something about their shining surface and peculiar slippery feel that is quite individual.

Citrine, the yellow variety of quartz, is the gem most often confused with topaz and sold in place of it, but surely citrine is inferior in richness and delicacy of color, as well as much cheaper in price. Attempts are still being made to effect standardization of gem names, particularly citrine and topaz.

The derivation of the word topaz is uncertain. The original name was applied to the variety of olivine now known as peridot. Conversely, the word chrysolite, another present-day name for olivine, was once used to indicate the true topaz. A probable source of the word topaz is the Sanskrit *tapas*, meaning "fire," for some of its colors merit such an appellation.

Topaz is an aluminum silicate containing fluorine and water, which indicate an origin through the action of hot acid gas. It is found mostly in pegmatites, granitic rocks, and in the placer deposits accumulating from their disintegration. Topaz is a frequent associate of tin ore, and the presence of either one is a useful indication of the other.

Crystals of topaz (Figs. 20 and 80) are distinctive in appearance, since they have exceptionally smooth faces, sharp edges, and a large base. Topaz has an extremely easy cleavage parallel to the base, so that a crystal may be split into any number of thin slabs with little trouble. This fragility is somewhat offset by great hardness. Among precious stones topaz ranks fourth in hardness; hence it resists the abrasive effects of ordinary use.

The relatively common occurrence of topaz in large crystals (see Fig. 80) keeps the cost of large cut stones low. A piece weighing 13 pounds was used as a doorstop by a London merchant until its identity was revealed and it was removed to the British Museum of Natural History. The enormous stone known as the Braganza diamond, which is among the treasures of Portugal, is believed to be topaz, but for a long time no one competent to form an opinion on it has been allowed to examine this 1,680-carat gem. Topaz gems of the most fascinating colors may be seen in the great mineral collections of our larger cities.

Brazil produces topaz of a rich yellow-brown color— called *imperial topaz* in that country—as well as most of the stones that are altered in color. Fancy pink topaz and

156

red topaz bring a high price, and blue stones are increasing in cost. Ceylon stands high in today's market. Russian and Siberian topazes are among the magnificent gems of

Fig. 80   Huge Crystal of Gem Topaz from Brazil
[Cranbrook Institute of Science.]

the world.   Other main foreign sources are Burma, Japan, Australia, the British Isles, and several of the gem-producing countries of Africa.

In the United States lovely blue topaz formerly came from San Diego County, California. Colorless and sherry-colored stones are found in the Thomas Mountains of Utah and are prized for their sparkle when cut. Splendid crystals have come from Colorado's mineral deposits; perhaps the largest complete topaz crystal ever found in North America was taken from Devil's Head in 1935. Several other states, especially those of New England, have produced topaz of gem quality, and the annual American output has on occasions exceeded $5,000. The blue topaz from Mason County, Texas, represents most of the stones being cut and marketed in the country today.

AXINITE

So named because of the wedge shape of its crystals (Fig. 27), axinite is a rare gem of unusual colors. It presents a choice of hues, including honey yellow, olive brown, and violet blue, which are accentuated by a strong dichroism that lends a charming evanescent effect. The luster is particularly pleasing.

The chemistry of axinite is complex, as the mineral is a hydrous silicate of boron and aluminum and contains several other elements substituting for one another. Axinite is approximately as hard as quartz. It is the only transparent gem besides kyanite that belongs to the triclinic system, the least symmetrical of the six main kinds of crystals. Axinite of the colors mentioned occurs in the French Alps, Tasmania, and several American localities.

ANDALUSITE

In its usual brown or green color, faceted andalusite closely resembles tourmaline of the same hue. The green gems are most striking when viewed along the main

158

crystallographic axis, for their strong dichroism causes bright flashes of red to gleam against the contrasting background.

Another interesting, though much less valuable, variety of andalusite is called *chiastolite*. It is never faceted, but when sections of it are polished they show a black cross which is due to the odd arrangement of the carbon matter present in the center. Chiastolite should not be confused with the completely cross-shaped "fairy stones" of staurolite, which owe their form to the intergrowth of two twinned crystals; both minerals are used in Christian countries as amulets.

Andalusite is an aluminum silicate with the same chemical formula as sillimanite and kyanite. Crystals of andalusite occur in square prisms belonging to the orthorhombic system. Transparent andalusite is somewhat harder than quartz, whereas chiastolite is considerably softer because of the difference of its interior.

The original source was the southern Spanish province of Andalusia, from which the mineral derives its name. Ceylon and Brazil furnish most of the current supply. Chiastolite comes from Siberia and Australia. The United States, particularly Massachusetts, yields both kinds.

SILLIMANITE

Occasional light-blue and green specimens of sillimanite appear in the gem trade. Their lack of distinction lies in the fact that they look much like several better-known gems of similar pale colors.

Crystals of sillimanite are long slender prisms of the orthorhombic system. Many of the stones are water-rounded, so that their original form is no longer evident. Sillimanite is slightly superior in hardness to quartz. In composition it is an aluminum silicate and has the same formula as andalusite and kyanite. Burma and Ceylon are the leading sources of gem material.

Sillimanite was named after Benjamin Silliman, a pioneer American geologist. Another name for it was *fibrolite* in reference to the typical fibrous structure of some of the material. Now, however, the name fibrolite is reserved for the fibrous variety only, some of which is grayish green or brown, resembling jade, and some of which shows a cat's-eye effect owing to the reflections from the tiny fibers.

KYANITE

Alone among all the minerals of the world in its variable hardness, kyanite has the curious ability of resisting the scratch of a knife in any direction except down the length of the crystal. This peculiar property is a sure means of identification.

Kyanite is one of few gems having the authentic color of blue sapphire. In its lighter blue tints it resembles aquamarine, and it may also be almost colorless; the prevailing hue, however, is so typical of kyanite as to suggest its name, which means "blue." ("Cyanite" is an obsolete spelling.)

An alternative name is *disthene*, meaning "double strength," in reference to the unequal hardness in different directions. The crystals are triclinic, in long blades, which usually have a concentration of color in the center, surrounded by a white margin. This color contrast is augmented by a strong dichroism.

160

Kyanite has exactly the same chemical formula as andalusite and sillimanite, all three being aluminum silicates. Because it possesses a very easy cleavage, and its cleavage surfaces show a pearly luster, uncut kyanite tends to exhibit a characteristic rippled surface unlike the more compact smoothness of other gems.

India and Burma produce kyanite in gem quality, as do Switzerland, Brazil, Kenya in East Africa, and the United States. Some beautiful kyanite of an uncommon green color comes from North Carolina.

SPHENE

With a dazzling surface luster and a display of rainbow colors excelling even diamond, sphene presents a magnificent appearance. So high, also, is its refractive index that a standard jeweler's refractometer fails to give a reading. In dispersion or fire sphene surpasses all the major gems with the sole exception of andradite garnet. In the extent of its double refraction sphene is even more impressive, standing alone at the top. A dichroscope shows marked differences in the hues of the individual rays transmitted through the darker stones.

With these astonishing optical properties, and a group of distinctive colors as well, sphene merits attention in any company of gems.

The name in Greek means "wedge" and clearly describes the odd-shaped monoclinic crystals shown in Fig. 24. Previously it was generally applied to the lighter colors, which are confined to green and yellow, while the now-discredited name "titanite" was used to indicate the darker, mostly brown, stones. At the present time sphene

161

is the accepted name of the species and includes the green, yellow, and brown colors, both light and dark.

As the word titanite suggests, this gem contains the chemical element titanium and is a silicate of titanium and calcium. The extraordinary optical characteristics of sphene are not matched by its other physical properties, for the hardness is considerably inferior to that of quartz, and the specific gravity is quite modest, almost exactly the same, in fact, as diamond, which too is notable for its low density as compared with its high refraction.

Gem sphene has come from Austria, Switzerland, Canada, and the northeastern part of the United States.

Chapter 4

Cabochon and Carved Gems

The amateur gem cutter of today begins, as did the earliest lapidary of ancient times, to work with the softer stones, fashioning them into cabochons before attempting any facet cutting, which demands a superior degree of mechanical skill and mathematical precision. *Cabochon* is defined as a stone cut in convex form, polished but not faceted; the term applies also to the style of cutting itself. Gems shaped in this manner are said to be cut cabochon, or *en cabochon* in the original French (derived from Latin).

The carving of gems involves an even greater ability than faceting does, because of the artistic talent required to sculpture figures, carve cameos, engrave intaglios and seals, and to create other ornamental forms of beauty and objects of usefulness in infinite variety.

Cabochon and carved gems are appropriately and conveniently discussed together, because in general the same stones are selected for both types of cutting. Although any gem may, of course, be cut in almost any way—for example, the carved diamond in the Chicago Natural History Museum—the usual media for cabochons and

163

carvings are opaque and translucent stones whose appeal lies in their attractive color, curious markings or mottling, or distinctive optical effects. These materials, it will be noted, do not exceed quartz in hardness. They are described by species in the rest of this chapter, which follows (with a few unavoidable exceptions) the order of minerals given in the seventh edition of *Dana's System of Mineralogy*.[1]

METALLIC GEMS

Metallic gems are judged by their luster, not by their chemical composition. Most gems contain a large percentage of some metal, such as aluminum, iron, or copper, but its presence is seldom manifested in the appearance of the stone. Among the common minerals a *metallic luster* is so frequent that it is used as the major criterion for classification in most schemes of determinative mineralogy; but only two gems, pyrite and hematite, have a luster like that of a typical metal.

Pyrite

The brass-yellow color of pyrite has deceived prospectors so often that they have given it the name "fool's gold." The name pyrite is derived from the Greek and refers to the sparks that fly when a specimen is struck.

Pyrite is a ubiquitous mineral, having been formed under every kind of circumstance and in almost every type of geologic body all over the world. It is an iron sulfide,

[1] Palache, Berman, and Frondel, Harvard University. Published by John Wiley and Sons, Inc., New York. Volume I, 1944.

used as an ore of iron in only a few places because it contains too small a proportion of the metal; however, it has been on occasion an important source of sulfur.

It may be one of the most handsomely crystallized of

Fig. 81   Handsome Group of Striated Pyrite Crystals
[Ward's Natural Science Establishment.]

the isometric minerals, occurring in a distinctive form called the pyritohedron and in cubes that are often striated in opposite directions on adjacent faces.   (See Fig. 81.) As is true of other common minerals, however, it is usually massive.

One novel way in which pyrite is set in jewelry is in a single cluster of small natural crystals.   Most cut and polished pyrite is sold under the trade name "marcasite." Real *marcasite*, which rarely appears in jewelry, is a very similar mineral, which has the same chemical formula but crystallizes in the orthorhombic system.

Hematite

Although it has been cut in a miscellany of faceted and cabochon shapes, even including beads to serve as an unconvincing substitute for black pearls, hematite makes its most frequent appearance in jewelry as intaglios for men's signet rings. For this purpose it is an excellent material; the design, usually the head of a warrior, is incised by hand below the surrounding polished surface.

The dark-gray color of such a highly reflecting opaque gem belies its true color, which is not seen until the stone is scratched or broken. Then the cherry-red hue of the mineral powder appears, and the origin of the name hematite, which comes from the Greek word meaning "bloodlike," becomes obvious. Usually hematite is red because it is already in a finely divided state; only crystals and hard masses are gray or black. Common hematite is found in numerous forms, such as micaceous, earthy, and fibrous.

Hematite is of tremendous significance to our industrial age, since it is the chief ore of iron in the world's vastest iron mines, those of the Lake Superior region. Hematite is ferric iron oxide; it crystallizes in the hexagonal system. The gemstone from Cumberland, England, has the highest reputation. Other sources include the island of Elba and the Scandinavian countries of Sweden and Norway. Hematite has been widely sold in the United States as "Alaskan diamond."

Four of the nonmetallic gems that are cut into cabochons or are carved—turquoise, feldspar, lapis lazuli, and jade—may be regarded as major gems, at least from an historical viewpoint. Nevertheless, the others described here are also well worthy of study, and some of them are pushing rapidly into prominence.

Smithsonite

When stained by the presence of impurities, the mineral smithsonite, which is white when pure, takes on various attractive colors. The translucent green or bluish-green material, sometimes banded (Fig. 82), is the most pleasing and has become a fairly well-known gem.

Smithsonite is a zinc carbonate, the zinc being replaced in part by other elements. Like related carbonates, of which it is the hardest, smithsonite crystallizes in the hexagonal system, though rarely in visible crystals. Its very sensitive cleavage in three directions tends to add a pearly luster to the vitreous luster of the unbroken surface. In some mines smithsonite is an important ore of zinc and represents a surface alteration (often indirectly) from sphalerite, the primary zinc sulfide, which is itself a gem mineral.

The stone was named after James Smithson, the English chemist who was born in France and established the Smithsonian Institution in the United States. It may be remarked that this mineral was formerly called "calamine" in Great Britain; American "calamine" (now named hemimorphite) is an entirely different zinc mineral.

167

Material good enough for jewelry comes from Kelly, New Mexico; Laurium, Greece; Santandar, Spain; and Tsumeb, South-West Africa.

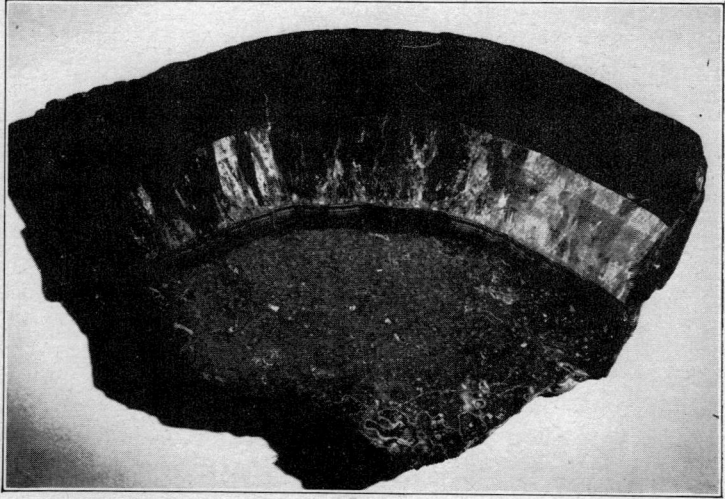

Fig. 82   Polished Slab of Banded Smithsonite
[Ward's Natural Science Establishment.]

Malachite

For richness of beauty, the silky banded green of malachite is unexcelled in the mineral kingdom. Its softness prevents its use in rings and other articles of jewelry that are subjected to much wear, but its bright opaque color makes it eminently suitable for pins, necklaces, and buttons. As a favorite stone of Czarist Russia, malachite was extravagantly carved into bowls, table tops, vases, and jewel boxes.

168

The agatelike banding, superbly shown in Fig. 83, is due to slow deposition from solution, for malachite is a secondary mineral occurring where copper ores have undergone certain processes of weathering that involve the

Fig. 83   Banded Gem Malachite
[Ward's Natural Science Establishment.]

addition of carbonic acid.   Malachite is a basic carbonate of copper, and like all carbonates it effervesces in acid.

Malachite crystallizes in the monoclinic system, but it seldom appears in sharply defined crystals; it is usually seen in massive rounded shapes.   Most of the crystals of malachite that have been found were once crystals of azurite (a gem mineral of similar composition) which have altered with a fibrous effect to the more stable compound. These pseudomorphs are shown in Fig. 84.

The name comes from the Greek word for "mallow," the leaf of some varieties of that plant resembling malachite in color. Concentrically banded malachite of superb gem

Fig. 84   South African Group of Fibrous Malachite Crystals Altered from Azurite

[Ward's Natural Science Establishment.]

quality comes from the Belgian Congo; other sources include Arizona, South Australia, Rhodesia, South-West Africa, and the Ural Mountains. In these and other places malachite is a valuable ore of copper.

Azurite

Although it occurs with malachite, alters to it, and has much the same properties, azurite nevertheless presents as striking a contrast in color as can be imagined. Its azure-blue color, from which it gets its name, is as brilliant as the green of malachite. Although not as abundant as malachite, azurite also is a widespread and useful ore of copper; it is, like malachite, a basic carbonate of copper, but the two have slightly different chemical formulas. The monoclinic crystals of azurite are not uncommon, though most azurite is massive. Azurite changes slowly to malachite (Fig. 84) under normal conditions. When both minerals have grown together, the resulting gem is called *azurmalachite*, which is used more frequently as an ornamental stone than azurite alone.

Variscite

The color of variscite, usually light green to bluish green, resembles some hues of turquoise, and the two stones have often been confused. But variscite year by year is becoming more conspicuous as a distinct American gem with a personality of its own. An observer promptly focuses his attention on the handsome polished nodules of Utah variscite in mineral cabinets, and cabochons cut from such pieces are appearing more often in jewelry. The recent phenomenal growth of the variscite industry is the result of a large production of rough material for the mineral collectors' market.

The only large deposits of variscite are in northern Utah, although the mineral was found long ago in Saxony and named after Variscia, a Roman name for the district. In Utah the variscite specimens occur in sedimentary rocks in brownish or gray nodules or concretions, in which are combined several minerals of similar appearance, as well as a great variety of other minerals—the whole showing intricately veined patterns. Cut pieces of variscite that include parts of the matrix are called *amatrix*, a word constructed from "American matrix." Patriotic pride has also attached the superfluous name *utahlite* to the pure variscite.

Variscite is a hydrous aluminum phosphate, colored by chromium, vanadium, and iron. It crystallizes in the orthorhombic system but is usually massive.

Turquoise

The present American vogue for turquoise coincides with a marked extension of the world's supply. Even the excited search for new deposits, however, has failed to meet the greatly increased demand. The gem consequently has been rising in price even more than the exigencies of inflation warrant.

Turquoise has completed another cycle in its long history of repeated lapses from and returns to favor. Yet with certain races it has always been popular. The oldest dated piece of jewelry is said to be an Egyptian bracelet set with turquoise, which probably came from the ancient mines of the Sinai Peninsula. The highest grade of turquoise known has come from deposits near Nishapur in the Iranian province of Khorosan; small wonder that the Persians have regarded it as their national gem! Turquoise has long been used throughout the Middle East as an amulet to protect horses from falling. In the jewelry and ornaments of Tibet turquoise is characteristically associated with coral, with which it contrasts nicely in color.

No peoples, however, have regarded turquoise with as much admiration as the Indians of the American South-west. They mined it industriously for centuries before the coming of the white man, and they struggled against their conquerors for possession of the deposits. The Navajos in particular treasured the stone more than any other article and still trade rugs, jewelry, or ponies for it.

The great mines near Los Cerillos in New Mexico were the largest and most famous in America, but, since the exhaustion of these sources, near-by states have in turn succeeded to the position of chief producer. Arizona, Nevada, Colorado, and California are the leading sources in today's market.

Turquoise may be blue or green or any blend of these two colors. A bright blue, often called robin's-egg blue, is regarded as the choicest hue. Some wearers, especially Indians, prefer a green color, even though it is much more common. Most blue stones have an unfortunate tendency to turn greenish with age as they absorb grease and oil or lose water. Numerous fraudulent attempts have been made to restore the faded color. Certain localities, however, are noted for the constant hue of the turquoise taken from them.

The cause of color in turquoise has not been established. Chemically, the mineral is a hydrous phosphate of aluminum and copper; iron partly replaces either or both of the other metals. Various beliefs have been expressed about the proportions of copper and iron needed to give specific colors, but analyses do not seem to sustain them.

Thought previously to be amorphous, turquoise was proved to crystallize in the triclinic system by the discovery in Virginia in 1912 of tiny but actual crystals. Everywhere else turquoise occurs in irregular veins, crusts, or lumps in broken rock that is generally volcanic in origin.

Thin wisps and small patches of other substances, mostly kaolin (a clay mineral) and limonite (an iron mineral), traverse almost all specimens. The resulting pattern is often attractive and is accepted as a sign of genuineness. When these veinlets are conspicuous, the material is sold as *turquoise-matrix*.

The rather waxy luster of turquoise serves to conceal scratches; it is fortunate, as the gem is not especially hard.

In addition to the places already mentioned, turquoise comes from several states of the Commonwealth of Australia and from Turkestan. The latter locality may have been responsible for the name of the gem, a French word referring either to Turkestan, the source, or Turkey, the market.

Odontolite or "bone turquoise" has often appeared as a substitute for true turquoise. This curious gem consists of the bones and teeth of animals, fossilized and colored blue or green by iron phosphate. Its organic texture reveals its origin. The name odontolite comes from two Greek words meaning "tooth stone."

Feldspar

The feldspar minerals constitute a group of similar species, closely related in chemical composition, crystallization, properties, and occurrence. Their scientific importance far exceeds their value in gemology. Nevertheless, the feldspar gems include several varieties of real charm.

The significance of the feldspars lies in their abundance, in the variability of their composition, and in the complexity of their crystallization. These factors combine to

174

make them extremely valuable as a basis for classifying rocks. With quartz they make up most of the bedrock surface of the earth. Unlike quartz, which is remarkably constant in chemical composition, they vary enough to serve as a fundamental means of differentiation among rocks that contain them. A specimen of feldspar the composition of which is known can be very useful in classifying the rock from which it came. Elaborate methods have been worked out for determining the composition of feldspars by microscopic examination of their crystallization, particularly their twinning, and entire books have been published on this subject. The name that is applied to a given igneous rock depends mainly upon the kind and amount of feldspar that is present.

Feldspar is commonly divided into two main types—the so-called *potash feldspars*, including orthoclase and microcline, and the *plagioclase feldspars*, which form a continuous series within themselves. All are silicates of aluminum, having potassium, sodium, and calcium as other major constituents. Orthoclase belongs to the monoclinic system and the rest are triclinic, but there is little difference in the shapes of the crystals, which appear in Figs. 23, 26, and 85. A prominent feature of the triclinic feldspars is their multiple twinning. Taking place on a small scale, this repeated twinning consists of countless parallel planes within the crystal and gives rise to a row of closely spaced lines or striations (sometimes visible only with a microscope) on the surface. When two or more kinds of twins are present, the structure may form a network pattern. The interference of light reflected from such twin planes is a major cause of the unusual optical effects that distinguish many of the feldspar gems. The close relation-

175

ship between the members of the feldspar group makes it possible for most of the gem varieties to occur in more than one species, because almost all the feldspar gems owe their distinctive characteristics to structural peculiarities,

Fig. 85   Amazonstone Crystals from near Pikes Peak, Colorado
[Ward's Natural Science Establishment.]

and these are seldom restricted to only one species of feldspar.

A conspicuous property of feldspar is the presence of two pronounced cleavages which are exactly or almost at right angles to each other. Feldspar is inferior to quartz in hardness; orthoclase is the standard for number 6 on Mohs' scale.

Besides being cut into gems, feldspar is widely used as a binder and a glaze in the manufacture of porcelain. Some

176

is used in glass-making. When regarded as the mineral that by the processes of weathering contributes more than any other to the formation of soil, feldspar takes on its full stature as a vital substance in the world we know.

Orthoclase. Occupying the first place among the feld-spar gems, *moonstone* has long been a favorite in fine jewelry and is perfectly adapted for beads, necklaces, and pins, though not durable enough for rings. Its soft radiance, like the glow of summer moonlight, has a quiet appeal that is never tiring. Moonstone usually appears white and rather milky until it is held in a favorable position, when a lovely sheen sweeps across its face in a subdued flush of light, which is bluer, the choicer the gem.

This optical effect is known as *schillerization*. It results from an intimate intergrowth called *microperthite*—a combination of two kinds of feldspar, orthoclase and plagioclase. The orthoclase constitutes most of the material and acts as a host for thin layers of albite (a kind of plagioclase). The presence of these layers tends to induce a separation or parting along them, and the reflection of light from such surfaces causes the schillerization. The spacing of these layers determines the color of the sheen. A moonstone must be oriented properly to reflect light; consequently it is always cut with a fairly steep, rounded top and a base that is parallel to the reflecting layer of albite.

Beautiful blue moonstone is found in Burma. Most of the good gems, however, come from Ceylon, where they are found in gravels and swamps, as well as in the original rock itself. Madagascar and Tanganyika Territory are other sources of moonstone. Switzerland was formerly a producing locality.

Not all moonstones have the composition just mentioned. Some are varieties of albite and some are varieties of oligoclase and will be discussed later under those members of the plagioclase series of feldspars. There is also a *pink moonstone*, which is a variety of scapolite, and a moonstone of inferior quality which is a variety of quartz. But the true moonstone is feldspar, and most of it consists largely of orthoclase.

Two other varieties of orthoclase, both of them transparent, are also used as gems.

A colorless, virtually pure, orthoclase that appears at its best when faceted has come mainly from Switzerland but is now quite rare. It was named *adularia* after the Adular Mountains, which formerly included the St. Gotthard region, the actual source.

Clear yellow orthoclase has been found in Madagascar within recent years. It owes its fine color to a small distribution of ferric iron oxide and makes attractive faceted stones. Pure orthoclase, such as adularia, is a silicate of potassium and aluminum.

Microcline. Like orthoclase, microcline is a so-called *potash* or *alkali feldspar* and has the same chemical formula. It crystallizes, however, in the triclinic system; its name refers to the small inclination by which the two cleavages differ from the right angle that they have in orthoclase, which means "straight cleavage."

Amazonstone (or *amazonite*) is the only gem variety of microcline and is also the only green feldspar. Owing to its color, which ranges from bluish green through bright green to greenish gray, it resembles jade and is often mistaken for it. The name amazonstone itself is the result of an error, for the mineral does not occur near the Amazon

178

River, but originally in the Ural Mountains. The one outstanding locality for amazonstone is the Pikes Peak region of central Colorado. When crystals from there, similar to those shown in Fig. 85, were displayed for sale at the Centennial Exposition in Philadelphia in 1876, their size and quality forced the Russian material off the market. Amazonstone also comes from Norway, Madagascar, and the state of Virginia. It has been cut into beads and other rounded forms. It cannot be carved like jade, however, because of its easy cleavages.

Plagioclase. The term plagioclase covers a completely isomorphous series of triclinic feldspar minerals, which grade into one another without any break. For convenience mineralogists have divided them arbitrarily into six species, which have no significance except that each expresses a given range of chemical composition. The optical and other physical properties change slowly as the composition changes.

The plagioclases are often called the *soda-lime feldspars*, because they run from albite, an aluminum silicate with sodium (soda), to anorthite, an aluminum silicate with calcium (lime). The progressive variation from albite to anorthite is not merely a substitution of sodium by calcium but is more complex, involving a change in aluminum and silicon as well.

Including the intermediate members of the series, the plagioclases are named albite, oligoclase, andesine, labradorite, bytownite, and anorthite. Each of the end-members embraces 10 per cent of the whole, and each of the others covers 20 per cent.

Three of these six plagioclases may be represented among the gems.

179

Albite. Referred to as a *sodic plagioclase* or an *alkali feldspar,* according to one's viewpoint, albite generally is similar in occurrence to the other alkali feldspars, orthoclase and microcline. The word albite comes from the Latin and means "white," its color.

A rare variety of albite called *peristerite,* from Canada and Madagascar, shows a play of colors when held in a certain position, owing to the interference of light that is reflected from twinning surfaces having a restricted orientation within the stone. Since the orientation varies with the composition of the feldspar, this interesting effect is not frequently seen in albite.

Some albite also occurs as *moonstone*

Oligoclase. In addition to a small part of the *moonstone* that is used in jewelry, oligoclase furnishes some transparent colorless stones that are attractive when faceted. Its chief contribution to gemology, however, is the variety *sunstone,* a perfect antithesis to the delicate loveliness of moonstone. The golden gleams of red and yellow that give sunstone its apt name come from light reflected from tiny flakes of hematite (a common iron mineral) distributed in a regular manner through the stone. The spangles disappear if the stone is heated and reappear only if the stone is cooled slowly enough. This gem is also known as *aventurine feldspar* from its resemblance to the original aventurine, which was the artificial glass containing copper crystals and now known as "goldstone." The richest sunstone comes from Norway where it is a popular gem. Other specimens are found in Siberia and in Modoc County, California.

Labradorite. As far as the feldspars are concerned, the iridescent play of colors resulting from the interference

180

of light rays reaches a culmination in labradorite. This common and abundant mineral, occurring in masses that weigh millions of tons, ordinarily gray or white at its best, becomes transformed on rare occasions, when the structure permits, into a sheet of brilliant hue. Across the gray surface sweeps a rush of blue or green, as bright as a peacock's feather—the same optical phenomenon is responsible in both instances—or of golden red or yellow. The primary cause of this effect is the repeated twinning in the mineral, the layers of which lie in the direction of the least favorable of the two chief feldspar cleavages.

Labradorite was named after its discovery along the coast of Labrador in the 18th century. It is found in islands off shore, and in Newfoundland and Quebec, and in Russia, but gem material forms only the smallest fraction of the rock. Labradorite must be cut with a flat surface to show its colors properly.

Sodalite

Although it will be mentioned as one of the four opaque blue minerals that constitute the major part of the rock-gem known as lapis lazuli, sodalite in some places is sufficiently homogeneous to be considered a distinct gem. The pleasing color is a deeper blue than that of lapis lazuli and somewhat more violet.

In chemical composition sodalite is a silicate of sodium, aluminum, and chlorine, and it crystallizes in the isometric system. Localities noted for masses of sodalite are three provinces of Canada—Ontario, Quebec, and British Columbia—and Litchfield, Maine. Crystals have been found at Mount Vesuvius and material of colors other than blue occurs elsewhere, but only the blue massive sodalite serves in jewelry and is carved into ornamental objects.

Lapis Lazuli

The "sapphire" of the Bible, lapis lazuli, was the most-prized blue gem of ancient times, not only for personal adornment but also for ornaments and inlaying. Assyrian and Babylonian jewelry and seals of lapis lazuli are in the most primitive forms. Chinese lapidaries have long carved from it small articles, of which snuff bottles are the most interesting. In Europe and America it is cut most often into beads and into stones for pins.

Like other opaque gems, lapis lazuli depends for its popu-larity upon its color, which is unrivaled among blue stones. It is, however, not merely a rich blue but spangled with gold and white, resembling, according to Pliny, the star-bedecked night sky.

Its variegated pattern is due to the fact that lapis lazuli, alone among the crystalline gems, is not a single mineral, but a rock consisting of an aggregate of several minerals. It was formed by the metamorphic action of a magma body on impure limestone. The molten rock recrystallized the limestone to marble and disseminated through it a number of new minerals. Any given specimens therefore contain different proportions of these minerals.

The most important constituents of lapis lazuli are the blue minerals, for they are chiefly responsible for its beauty. Four of them are known, all members of the *feldspathoid group*, so called because they are produced instead of feld-spar in rocks that have abundant alkalies but insufficient silica. Hauynite has recently been proved to be the main

182

constituent, and the others are lazurite, sodalite, and nose-lite. One or more of the four may be present, since they are isomorphous and partly replace one another. Chemically, they are silicates of sodium and aluminum; some necessary calcium, chlorine, and sulfur are distributed variously among them. They crystallize in the isometric system but usually in shapeless masses. Their hardness is moderate, but opaque stones do not need to be as hard as transparent ones which show scratches easily.

The golden color is supplied by flecks of pyrite, the iron-sulfide mineral known as "fool's gold." Its presence proves the genuineness of lapis lazuli, although its popular appeal changes with the fashions.

Another common mineral, calcite, furnishes the white wisps and veins. At least half a dozen other well-known minerals have been found in specimens of lapis lazuli.

The name of the gem, now often shortened simply to *lapis*, was given to it in the Middle Ages, partly from the Latin word for "stone" and partly from the Arabic word meaning "blue"; its resemblance to our words lazurite and azure is obvious.

Until the past century lapis lazuli was doubly prized, for it formed the base of the wonderful blue pigment called ultramarine, since produced artificially.

Marco Polo visited and described the remarkable lapis lazuli mines of Badakhshan in Afghanistan in 1271. These mines have been worked for 6,000 years; near-by deposits also yield ruby and spinel. Good lapis lazuli is found near Lake Baikal in Siberia. A paler quality is mined in the Chilean Andes. Other sources include Upper Burma and San Bernardino County, California. The newest locality for good gems is near the top of North Italian Mountain in central Colorado.

Prehnite

Translucent light-green prehnite of various hues is occasionally cut as cabochons. The uncut crystals, which belong to the orthorhombic system, are distinctive rounded aggregates which furnish an easy clue to the identity of the mineral. Another green variety of prehnite occurs in a more compact manner resembling jade. Prehnite is a hydrous silicate of aluminum and calcium. It was the first mineral to be named (in 1783) in honor of a person, Colonel von Prehn, who brought specimens from South Africa to Europe. Prehnite is found with datolite, also a gem mineral, and with zeolites in cavities in volcanic rocks, where it has been deposited by solutions after the consolidation of the lava. Leading sources are New Jersey, Connecticut, the Lake Superior region, France, and China.

Chlorastrolite is a prehnite-like mineral mixture found in Isle Royale National Park, the largest island in Lake Superior. It makes attractive cabochons. Exactly a century ago it was recognized as a mixture rather than a single mineral, but the name persists.

Jade

Jade stars in a double role. It represents two distinct minerals, which in some ways are very different, yet in other ways are so much alike that only mineralogists try to discriminate between them. Moreover, a number of

184

other materials that somewhat resemble them often are improperly called jade.

The true jade minerals are *jadeite* and *nephrite*. From an artistic and historical standpoint they are best treated together, for the term jade, which combines both, has great significance. From the view of the scientist, however, they should be described separately. Attention will first be directed to the similarity between them by a discussion of jade as a single substance.

As such it has always been regarded by the Chinese as the noblest of gems. It occupies a place in their art and their lore that has no counterpart elsewhere. The history of China, its triumphs and disasters, its prosperity and decline, can be read in the styles of jade carving that have gradually developed over the millennia and reflect the mood, the thought, and the action of a great civilization.

In a general way, but with highly important variations, the trend has been from crude and simple markings to involved geometric patterns, then to free-flowing designs that expressed religious symbolism, finally to sculptured forms, which have become increasingly elaborate in modern times. Examples of Chinese jade are treasured in many museums and private collections (Figs. 86 and 87). Some pieces are so intricately worked that they are almost beyond the comprehension of the Western mind. The collections in New York and Chicago should be seen by everyone fascinated by this material.

Ancient races of both hemispheres used jade to make their axes, knives, and other implements and weapons, although this practice was early abandoned in China, except when objects such as bowls and plates could be both

185

useful and beautiful. The natives of New Zealand specialized in carving weird human figures in jade, but they too used it in numerous other ways, as is proved by their name

Fig. 86   Jade Figure from the Chang Wen Ti Collection

Fig. 87   Chinese Carved Jade

[Chang Wen Ti.]

for jade, axe-stone. The inhabitants of Central America and adjacent countries used thousands of pieces of jade for utilitarian and religious purposes. Two fine jade carvings from Central America are shown in Figs. 88 and 89.

186

Fig. 88   Mayan Figure, Honduras

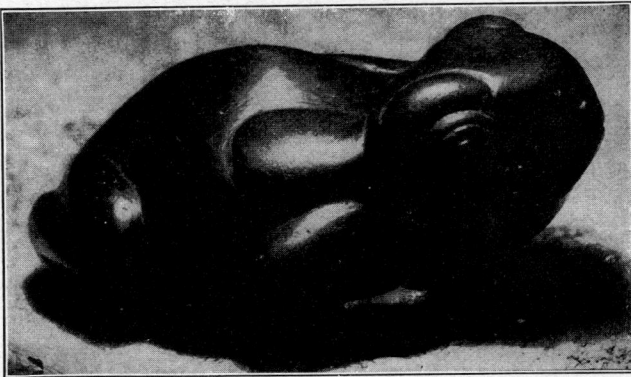

Fig. 89   Aztec Toad, Mexico

Native American Jade Carvings

[Middle American Research Institute.]

Many jade articles have been recovered among the prehistoric lake dwellings in Switzerland.

With the possible exception of diamond, more books have been written about jade than about any other gem. The noted 100-chapter "Sung" catalogue of jade in the collection of Emperor Kao-tsung, alleged to have been published in China in 1176, may be merely an 18th-century forgery.

The name for jade and the word for precious stone are the same in the Chinese language. Our word jade comes from the Spanish word for it, *piedra de ijada*, meaning "colic stone," which refers to its supposed value as a cure for illness.

The color of jade runs all the way through the spectrum. If chemically pure, jade should be white, but it seldom is. Jade may have impurities sufficient to make it blue, yellow, or almost any hue. A mottled distribution of color is the rule in most specimens. Green is so frequently the color of jade that it is sometimes carelessly regarded as the only color. Some colors are more typical of jadeite, which comes in a wider range, whereas others are more often seen in nephrite; it is usually difficult or impossible to distinguish between the two kinds by sight, especially with very old pieces, known as *tomb jade*, that have been buried in graves and oxidized brown. At its best jade may be quite translucent, but it is usually opaque.

The chief characteristic of jade is its extraordinary toughness. In hardness, as measured by the scratch test, it never exceeds quartz, but it is so immune to breakage that it often resists really violent treatment that would destroy almost any other mineral substance. This durability gives jade the essential quality for which it has been valued for many centuries and results from the fact that jade consists of a compact aggregate of crystals so intimately intergrown that they refuse to be separated.

A curious property of jade is its resonance, reported in the oldest Chinese records known to us. The ability of jade to yield melody must surely have added to its virtues in the hearts of the Chinese.

The source of both kinds of jade poses some interesting problems in geography. Only a part of the rough material is found in the original rock; the rest is taken from boulders whose place of origin often cannot be traced. Much more troublesome has been the difficulty faced by archaeologists and ethnologists in their attempts to determine the source of widespread articles of jade, especially in Central America, Mexico, and central Europe. Complex and improbable trade routes have been assumed in some instances to account for this distribution.

Jadeite. Of the two kinds of jade the more valuable is jadeite. It is considerably rarer than nephrite and brings a higher price when its identity is known. Emerald-green stones colored by chromium are called *imperial jade* and may approach transparency. *Mutton-fat jade* is also a favored color, and others include bright yellow, blood red, and mauve. These colors are almost always in streaks or patches associated with less choice colors. When jadeite is dark green or virtually black because of its high iron content, it is known as *chloromelanite*.

Jadeite belongs to the *pyroxene group* of minerals, so named because one of them was erroneously thought to be a "stranger in the domain of fire"—yet some of the pyroxenes are the most characteristic constituents of high-temperature igneous rocks. Other gem members of the group, described elsewhere in this book, include enstatite, diopside, and spodumene. Jadeite is a silicate of sodium and aluminum and contains a variable proportion of replacing elements, mainly calcium, magnesium, and iron. It crystallizes in the monoclinic system, but almost always in irregular masses; individual crystals are rarely seen.

The crystalline aggregate that gives jadeite its toughness possesses a granular texture, which in turn gives the surface a somewhat dimpled appearance. Though the rough surfaces are dull or waxy, the luster of cut and polished jadeite is vitreous. Jadeite is the harder and heavier of the two jade minerals; a test for specific gravity is often used to distinguish between them.

One of the characteristic gems of metamorphic origin, jadeite is found in dikes in a green serpentine rock. If it has been eroded out of place by streams or glaciers, it is found as scattered boulders.

It seems almost contradictory that little jadeite has ever been found in China. The material must have been imported from near-by countries long after nephrite was used. Most of the world's jadeite still comes from quarries discovered in the 13th century in the Myitkyina district in Upper Burma and is shipped to China by way of Rangoon. The rest of Chinese jadeite came from the mountains of Turkestan. Most other reported finds may be viewed suspiciously, for the whole matter of the identity and the sources of both kinds of jade needs restudy.

Nephrite. The more common of the two jades is nephrite, a member of the *amphibole group* of minerals. This group closely parallels the pyroxenes, to which jadeite belongs, and includes a similar range of elements but only one gem material instead of three as in the pyroxene group.

190

More specifically, nephrite fits into that part of the amphiboles which is represented by the *tremolite-actinolite series*, the members of which grade into each other according to the amount of iron present; when there is enough iron to color a specimen green, it is called actinolite. Both of them are better known in the form of asbestos, but when they are tough and compact they become nephrite. Chemically, nephrite is a silicate of calcium and magnesium, with some iron and water.

The name comes from the Greek word for "kidney," which implies the same curative power as the Spanish word for jadeite. New Zealand material is often called *greenstone*, but this is confusing because the same word has a different meaning to geologists.

Nephrite has a smaller range of color than jadeite but sufficient to satisfy most preferences. The green color is due to ferrous iron. Nephrite is usually more opaque than jadeite and hence is less highly valued. Whereas a rough piece of nephrite is as dull as a rough piece of jadeite, the polished surface takes on an oily instead of a vitreous luster.

Nephrite crystallizes in the monoclinic system. Its structure is distinctly fibrous, the individual fibers often being entwined in a most confusing way; nephrite is even tougher than jadeite. Much nephrite has a hornlike appearance.

Nephrite, like jadeite, is metamorphic in origin and is found in the parent rock, as well as in boulders.

China furnishes its share of nephrite. Although jadeite occurs in Turkestan, as mentioned before, nephrite is much more important there. It is also found west of Lake Baikal in south-central Siberia. The old question of the origin of the carved jade used by the Swiss lake dwellers and of similar pieces picked up elsewhere in Europe was solved by the discovery of nephrite at several places in Silesia. The Maoris of New Zealand obtained their nephrite mostly from boulders on South Island. Similar nephrite comes from Alaska, where tons of rough green and brown material are now being mined each summer and brought out by dog teams, airplanes, and small boats.

In 1946 nephrite moved into the leading place among American gems in terms of value of production, owing to the continued expansion of jade prospecting in Wyoming which began about ten years before. There has been a steady improvement in the color and translucency of the green stones, and the black ones are being found in larger sizes. Both kinds are being shipped to China for carving, though most of them are still cut in the United States. The specimens are found mostly as loose boulders on the surface of the ground, but ledges of jade are also known.

Mention should be made of the nephrite deposit in Monterey County, California, where jade is collected as boulders by skin divers working offshore, as well as from solid rock on the land.

Rhodonite

Russian lapidary art boasts among its achievements the creation of lavish carvings in rhodonite. As large an object as a royal sarcophagus has been made from it, and a favorite gift at court was a rhodonite Easter egg. This opaque pink mineral, appropriately named from the Greek word for "rose," is moderately hard, and when compact it takes a satisfying polish, suitable for beads or cabochons.

As a manganese silicate, rhodonite is a primary mineral which readily alters to black oxides that by the geologic processes of concentration often become important ores of manganese. The black veins so common in rhodonite are evidence that alteration has already begun.

Although it is often referred to as a member of the pyroxene group of minerals, rhodonite can claim only a first-cousinly relationship to them. It crystallizes in the triclinic system, and occurs both massive and in crystals (Fig. 28) having two distinct cleavages.

Translucent crystals of rhodonite are found in Sweden. Most of the material used in Russia was quarried in the Ural Mountains. Other massive rhodonite comes from New South Wales, and some gems have been cut from the unusual zinc-bearing rhodonite at Franklin, New Jersey.

Chrysocolla

Pretty gems for pendants and bracelets are cut from translucent chrysocolla, which is found in delicate hues of green and blue. The luster is either vitreous or enamel-like. Chrysocolla is a hydrous copper silicate with a variable composition, so that the chemist has difficulty in assigning an exact formula to it. Chrysocolla is very finely crystalline, like chalcedony quartz, and has not yet been assigned to any particular crystal system.

In the upper zone of copper deposits where it has been formed by the alteration of primary minerals, chrysocolla is associated with two other gems, azurite and malachite, and serves as a minor ore of copper. It has a world-wide

193

distribution; American gems come especially from Arizona and New Mexico.

The name has an interesting origin. It comes from two Greek words meaning "gold glue," because chryso-colla, or much more probably a mineral resembling it, was believed used by ancient jewelers to solder gold.

Idocrase

Until its present name was internationally agreed upon about a decade ago, this mineral was better known as "vesuvianite," from its earliest recognized occurrence on Mount Vesuvius. Of all the gems it is perhaps the most difficult to classify according to the predominant mode of cutting. The transparent crystals of prevailingly green, yellow, and brown tones, are eminently desirable for faceting. The variety *californite,* however, occurs in compact green masses like jade. The large amount of this latter material that has been cut and polished in the United States during recent years has been the deciding factor in placing idocrase among the cabochon gems.

Chemically, idocrase is a hydrous silicate of calcium and aluminum with a complex formula that allows for the presence of magnesium and iron; other, rarer, elements include fluorine, boron, and beryllium. Crystals of ido-crase belong to the tetragonal system and often show well-developed square prisms (Fig. 16) with striated faces. The name of the mineral comes from two Greek words mean-ing "form-mixing" because the crystals were mistaken for those of other minerals.

During the metamorphism of limestone to marble, a number of new minerals, including idocrase, crystallize.

194

The gem associates of idocrase include diopside, garnet, and tourmaline.

Californite is found in Siskiyou, Tulare, and Fresno counties in California. When discovered earlier in the Swiss Alps it was believed to be jade. Transparent gem idocrase comes from Mount Vesuvius and Piedmont Province in Italy, the Tirol, Switzerland, and Siberia. Superior-quality gem crystals were found in 1946 in an asbestos quarry in northern Vermont.

Zoisite

Two types of zoisite have been cut and polished for their attractive appearance. One is a rose-colored variety, called *thulite* from the old name for Norway, where it is chiefly found; it also occurs in the Italian province of Piedmont. Thulite owes its pleasing color to magnanese and is cut into cabochons, slabs, and small ornaments.

The other material is really a mixture of several minerals, of which zoisite is the chief. Known as *saussurite* and named after the Swiss geologist Horace B. deSaussure, it is the product of the decomposition of feldspar. Because of its resemblance to jade it is substituted on occasion for that more valuable gem.

Zoisite itself is a hydrous silicate of calcium and aluminum; it belongs to the *epidote group* of minerals but is the only one that crystallizes in the orthorhombic system.

Staurolite

Although an occasional transparent brown pebble of staurolite is taken from the diamond-bearing sands of

Brazil and faceted into a stone for jewelry, the mineral is in gemology more a charm than a gem. Known as "cross stone" and "fairy stone," it has been associated with the activities of legendary beings and is widely used as an amulet. It seems to be the only gem besides pearl that is worn in its original state, with no treatment necessary except drilling so that it may be hung on a chain or sus-

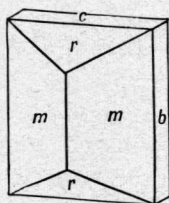 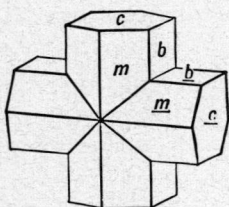 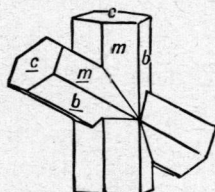

| Fig. 90 | Fig. 91 Twin | Fig. 92 Twin |
| Single | | |

Crystals of Staurolite

[From Hurlbut *Dana's Manual of Mineralogy*, copyright 1941.]

pended from a swivel. Some specimens, of course, are polished to remove foreign particles adhering to them.

The crosslike twin crystals of staurolite are unique and unmistakable. They consist of two orthorhombic crystals (Fig. 90) which penetrate each other; some pairs cross nearly at right angles (Fig. 91) and others cross at about 60 degrees (Fig. 92). In color they are reddish brown or brownish black; the choicest specimens are rather red, translucent, and symmetrically formed. These crossed crystals should not be confused with the chiastolite variety of andalusite, which owes its cross to inclusions of carbon.

196

Staurolite is at least as hard as quartz, but this hardness has little practical value inasmuch as the stone is so seldom cut. Chemically, staurolite is a hydrous silicate of aluminum and ferrous iron, but even reasonably pure specimens are rare.

Staurolite is a characteristically metamorphic mineral, associated with other gems, including garnet, tourmaline, kyanite, and sillimanite. Excellent crystals are found in Switzerland; others come from Germany, Czechoslovakia, France, Scotland, and Brazil. In several places in the United States, especially along the South Atlantic Coast in Georgia, North Carolina, and Virginia, they are picked up in abundance.

Dumortierite

Massive, opaque, blue or violet dumortierite takes a fine polish and has been cut into flat stones and cabochons. The mineral is found also in an attractive pink color with strong dichroism, resembling tourmaline. It is most valuable, however, as a raw material for the best refractory porcelain, and as such it is extensively mined in Nevada and California. Gemmy stones are found in these and a number of other localities throughout the world.

Dumortierite was named for a French paleontologist, Eugene Dumortier. It is a silicate of aluminum and boron and forms in pegmatite dikes and metamorphic rocks. Although it belongs to the orthorhombic system it seldom shows distinct crystals; frequently it is found in fibrous crystalline aggregates radiating from a center.

197

Practically all the gems thus far discussed have been carved, more or less frequently, into ornamental objects, some of which have utilitarian value also. There is, however, a small group of minerals, often mentioned in books on gemology, that are almost never suitable for personal adornment but serve a wider ornamental and decorative purpose. Not to overlook them, a single paragraph is devoted to each, but the reader is referred to books on economic mineralogy for more adequate descriptions of them.

Marble

The charm of marble lies in its infinite variety. So diverse is this substance that almost any random word-picture fits marble from some locality. Figure 29 shows dendritic marble. Chemically, marble is calcium carbonate (though seldom pure), and geologically, it is metamorphosed limestone. A large part of the marble used for such objects as pen stands is sold under the name "onyx," which properly applies only to the chalcedony variety of quartz, a very much harder and more durable mineral. Besides relative softness, marble is characterized by its effervescence in acid.

Gypsum

The massive variety of gypsum, which is calcium sulfate, is called *alabaster*, though in ancient times alabaster, as used in the Bible, meant the material that we now call marble. Owing to its softness the mineral is easily carved. Vases and boxes of white Italian alabaster are well known. In the United States, especially in Colorado, alabaster is worked into lamps and other articles that adapt themselves nicely to its white color and brown or gray veining. *Satin spar*, which occurs in monoclinic crystals like that in Fig. 25, has a fibrous structure; many necklaces fashioned from this variety of gypsum have been sold at tourist resorts, notably Niagara Falls.

Sepiolite (Meerschaum)

The German word meerschaum means "sea foam" and is properly descriptive of this porous, whitish mineral found floating in the sea. The material to which this name is applied seems to be a mixture of some amorphous substance and a fibrous mineral known as *sepiolite*, which is a hydrous silicate of magnesium. It is derived from the alteration of serpentine; by far the most important source is Asia Minor. Meerschaum, because it is easily carved and capable of taking a pleasing polish, has been used considerably for pipe bowls.

Serpentine

When mottled in dark and light green, corresponding in appearance to a serpent's skin, from which it gets its name, serpentine makes an attractive decorative stone because of its lively patterns and its oily or waxy luster. It is a hydrous silicate of magnesium and is found abundantly throughout the world as an alteration product of olivine and other magnesium silicates. It crystallizes in the monoclinic system, but no original crystals have ever been seen. Serpentine is usually found in masses consisting of a platy mineral known as *antigorite*. *Bowenite* is a compact variety of this same substance and resembles jade; material from China and New Zealand is carved and sold as jade. When serpentine is fibrous it is called *chrysotile*, which is the chief kind of commercial asbestos.

Miscellaneous Jadelike Minerals

Several minerals that resemble jade have already been discussed. Most of them are gemstones in their own right, a jadelike variety being an "added attraction." These minerals include quartz, feldspar, serpentine, prehnite, garnet, idocrase, zoisite, and sillimanite.

A few materials not otherwise mentioned in gemology have more or less frequently been carved and sold as jade. They may be appropriately described here under "Ornamental Stones."

Compact pieces of the mineral *pectolite*, a fusible hydrous silicate of calcium and sodium, are carved into ornaments and implements by the Eskimos of Alaska.

In a rather different category from pectolite belong some materials which are soft enough to be worked with a knife. They are familiar in cheap Oriental objects, but the names given to them are not standardized and are often confusing. Some of the materials themselves, moreover, are not homogeneous, and hence the same name may apply to several different natural mixtures of minerals.

Soapstone carvings, such as vases, ash trays, and animal figures, make up a large part of every stock of Chinese articles. Soapstone is the popular name for *steatite*, a soapy-feeling compact variety of *talc*, which is a monoclinic hydrous silicate of magnesium at the very bottom of the hardness scale. The mineral *saponite*, which is a hydrous silicate of aluminum and magnesium, also is called soapstone.

Similar to these (and including some steatite) is a material known as *agalmatolite*, though the name is seldom used; most of the objects made from it are called soapstone, "figure stone," or "pagoda stone." The last two names are appropriate because the Chinese use it so profusely for images and replicas of pagodas. Agalmatolite is actually *steatite*, *pinite*, *pyrophyllite*, or indefinite mixtures produced by the alteration or decomposition of various silicate minerals.

Chapter 5

Gems of the Silica Group

Silica is the chemical term for a stable compound of silicon and oxygen that occurs everywhere in both the organic and the inorganic world. Three minerals—quartz, tridymite, and cristobalite—each existing in several modifications, are composed of silica. A fourth mineral, opal, consists of silica and a varying amount of water. Of these, quartz and opal are among the most important of all gems. In addition, though not true minerals and hence not part of the silica group, there may properly be included in this chapter three kinds of natural glass containing high amounts of silica and having some use in gemology.

The quartz gems lose none of their beauty because they happen to belong to the most abundant of the mineral species. Besides many common and industrially useful varieties, quartz boasts a number of splendid gems, without which the jeweler's window as well as the mineral kingdom would be immeasurably poorer. A large part of the mineral specimens collected yearly in the United States by enthusiastic hobbyists, and most of those cut into gems by amateur and professional lapidaries, are quartz. In hardness quartz ranks number 7 in the standard scale and serves to demarcate the hard gemstones from the soft ones.

Gems are furnished by two main types of quartz, which differ mainly in the degree of fineness which their structure has assumed. The *crystalline* varieties—*quartz* proper —are rather glassy in appearance, are more or less transparent, and frequently occur in good crystals. The *cryptocrystalline* (*crypto* means "hidden") or *chalcedony* varieties do not show external faces but are nevertheless composed of exceedingly small crystals in a microscopically intimate aggregate which gives them a compact, flinty look. Much controversy has arisen about whether chalcedony should be regarded as a distinct mineral or as a fibrous variety of quartz containing trapped water. Its hardness, specific gravity, and other properties are slightly lower than those of crystalline quartz. Inasmuch as the general differences between the two are such as to make one (quartz) suitable for faceting and the other (chalcedony) for cutting into cabochons, in accordance with the major divisions of this book, it is becoming customary to refer to them as separate gem minerals.

QUARTZ

The typical crystal of quartz (Fig. 93) is easily recognized by its six sides which, when they are complete, come to a point at one or both ends. A frequent aid to identification is the presence of horizontal lines or striations on the prism faces. Quartz crystals range in size from tiny ones in groups to single crystals weighing a ton. Much quartz of the crystalline type is found in irregular masses that fail to show crystal faces; but the precise regularity prevails internally.

Fig. 93   Group of Quartz Crystals
[Ward's Natural Science Establishment.]

Amethyst

The most valuable quartz gem is amethyst. Its incomparable color varies from a delicate orchid to a glorious purple unsurpassed in the realm of nature. The name comes from the Greek word meaning "not drunken," supposedly because the stone was believed to prevent or cure intoxication; Pliny wrote that the name was given because the color approached but did not equal the hue of wine.

Until the discovery of large deposits of amethyst in South America, the stone was considerably more expensive. Only its relative abundance can account for the present reasonable cost of so lovely a gem. For amethyst has been highly praised for thousands of years, and from it have been carved works of art of the highest excellence. Those from Egypt include charms, vases, and shells; Etruscan and Roman specimens are principally intaglios of pale tint. Splendid examples of amethyst sculpture include a bust of Trojan which was taken from Berlin to Paris by Napoleon, the Blacas Medusa head, and miniature reproductions of the Apollo Belvedere, the Farnese Hercules, and the Laocoön groups.

One of the most famous pieces of historical jewelry is the necklace of fine amethyst beads worn by Queen Charlotte of England in the days before the gem began to lose its rarity. Catherine the Great was an ardent collector of amethysts. Her unrivaled collection of them was secured from mines in the Ural Mountains by thousands of slaves and laborers. The most beautiful amethysts were placed among the crown jewels, settings for which were designed by French jewelers, and they were the boast of Catherine's successors until many of the finest were sold in 1906. The rest are in the possession of the Soviet government, according to an inventory made in 1925 by a German mineralogist, who described them as "glowing fires."

The structure of amethyst represents an intricate arrangement of twinned particles. The color is usually in layers and patches, and seems to be due to iron present as an impurity.

Amethyst is the national gem of Uruguay. The deposits extend into neighboring Brazil and constitute the most notable source of amethyst in the world. Gems of the richest hue have come from Siberia. Ceylon and Japan have provided good crystals. In the United States fine specimens of amethyst have been found in half a dozen states; major places include Amherst County, Virginia, Alexander and Lincoln Counties, North Carolina, Jefferson County, Montana, and at Four Peaks, Gila County, Arizona.

Aventurine

This is perhaps the only gem named for its imitation. Several centuries ago a bowl of copper filings fell by accident into a pot of molten glass in a factory near Venice. The brightly colored glass was so attractive that it was made into ornaments and called aventurine, from the Italian word for "chance." Many years later a natural substance of similar appearance was discovered and was also named aventurine; it proved to be a variety of quartz. The imitation material is widely sold in novelty jewelry as "goldstone." Aventurine is usually green, brown, or red quartz, spangled with flakes of mica or hematite. The Soviet Union and India are the most noted sources.

Citrine

Yellow quartz is named citrine from the Latin word for "lemon," but its color is usually somewhat more brownish than that of the fruit. It looks so much like topaz that these two entirely distinct minerals have long been confused. The difference between them is still not thoroughly realized, even by many jewelers. The significant contrast between the two is really their cost; a purchaser cannot expect to find the much rarer true topaz in moderately priced jewelry, and therefore should assume that the word topaz when unqualified is usually being used incorrectly to mean citrine.

Ferric iron oxide is the cause of the color, which ranges from yellowish green to yellow and reddish orange. These hues are sometimes obtained by heating darker, inferior varieties of quartz. Brazil produces most of the world's supply of citrine, though some comes from Madagascar.

Rock Crystal

Clear lustrous quartz, without any color, is known as rock crystal. When first discovered high in the Alps it was believed to be a "kind of ice" (*krystallos*), that is, water permanently frozen into a definite form by the excessive cold. The word *crystal*, now applied to any regularly shaped mineral, came from this erroneous idea. So, in a sense, this variety of quartz was the original "crystal."

Under that name it appears as spheres (Fig. 94) for the hypnotic art of crystal gazing. Displayed in the United States National Museum is the largest crystal ball in the world, a perfect globe weighing 107 pounds. The extensive use of rock crystal in optical, radio, and radar location instruments is a phenomenon of World War II. Cut into thin plates it controls frequencies by means of its very rapid and very regular vibration. As crystals must be free from internal twinning, the supply is limited almost entirely to Brazil. Rock crystal is also used for eye-glasses on account of its hardness and for camera lenses because of its transparency to ultraviolet rays.

Its popularity as a gem is especially evident in the many bead necklaces that have been made from it. Rock

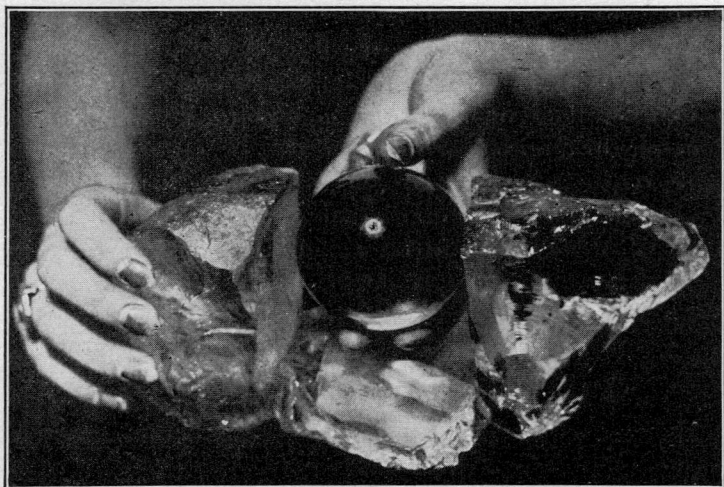

Fig. 94. Rock Crystal Sphere

The boulder from which it was cut was found in the soil at Philadelphia. [From Hawkins *The Book of Minerals*, copyright 1935.]

crystal seals and ornamental carvings are prized in leading museums.

Its abundance makes rock crystal the most common transparent gem. Great quantities of large crystals come from Brazil. Madagascar and Japan, as well as the Alpine countries of Europe, have furnished much high-quality material. The Arkansas deposits near Hot Springs are the most prolific in North America, and the exquisite little crystals called "Herkimer diamonds" that used to come in large numbers from Herkimer County, New York, are surely the choicest.

Rainbow Quartz

Rock crystal made iridescent by cracks which separate the light into its spectrum colors is known as *iris* or *rainbow quartz*. This minor variety can be imitated by the sudden cooling of a heated stone.

Milky Quartz

The presence of many liquid inclusions reduces the transparency of rock crystal and causes a milky appearance which justifies the name milky quartz.

Gold Quartz

During the great gold rushes of the 19th century a large quantity of milky quartz containing particles of gold and hence called gold quartz was cut for jewelry as souvenirs of the mining camps.

Sagenite

Rock crystal that encloses needlelike crystals of other minerals, such as tourmaline, rutile, actinolite, or goethite, constitutes the variety known as sagenite. Several names that are more romantic are also used—Venus's-hairstone, arrows of love, and Cupid's darts.

Cat's-Eye

When the inclusions of other minerals in quartz become so closely packed that they seem to predominate over the quartz itself, and especially when they are present in thin parallel fibers like asbestos, the chatoyant variety known as cat's-eye is formed. A band of light at right angles to the fibers follows the gem as it is turned. This stone should really be called *quartz cat's-eye* to distinguish it from cat's-eye of the chrysoberyl kind (already described under that species). The two gems resemble each other somewhat, but the chrysoberyl is superior in value because of its more lustrous beauty. Green, brown, and yellow quartz cat's-eye, mostly with a grayish cast, comes from Ceylon, India, and Germany.

Tiger's-Eye

When the quartz itself, rather than its inclusions, is fibrous, two other varieties of "eye stones"—tiger's-eye and hawk's-eye—are produced.

Tiger's-eye is unique among gems, a golden brown stone with wavy bands of light which move glowingly across the surface when it is rotated. Originally it was a blue kind of asbestos called crocidolite, but the coloring matter has been oxidized and the mineral completely replaced by quartz. Preservation of the earlier fibrous structure causes the handsome rippling effect known as chatoyancy. When first found, tiger's-eye (or *tiger eye*) brought a high price, which declined drastically upon the discovery of large deposits of the material. However, it still comes from only one place in the world, Griqualand West in

South Africa. Cut into cameos for men's rings, it has been one of the most popular stones of recent years.

Hawk's-Eye

Crocidolite similarly turned into quartz but without changing its blue color in the process is called hawk's-eye.

Rose Quartz

Its lovely hues of pink and rose red, caused by the presence of manganese, make rose quartz one of the prettiest of the translucent gemstones. It occurs in irregular masses without crystal faces. In spite of being very difficult to handle because it breaks into angular pieces with jagged edges, it is often worked into beads, small ornaments, and cabochons. The Scott mine near Custer, South Dakota, is a huge quarry of rose quartz, but material of ornamental quality is scarce even there. Other sources include South-West Africa and a few of the many deposits elsewhere that yield the more common quartz gems.

Smoky Quartz

A pleasant surprise is in store for everyone who looks for the first time through a crystal of smoky quartz and sees an apparently opaque black stone become a mysteriously hazy but rich shade of brown as the light comes through. The cause of this color is ascribed to radioactive emanations within the rocks. Smoky quartz has been found so frequently in association with uranium and other

211

radium-containing minerals that this relationship seems most plausible. Furthermore, clear rock crystal takes on a smoky hue when it is bombarded experimentally by X-rays and other powerful short-wave rays.

Lighter hues of smoky yellow, grading into citrine, are known as *cairngorm*, a Scottish name for a gem so popular in that country that it is regarded as a national stone. Smoky quartz grades in the other direction to a black stone known as *morion*, used occasionally in mourning jewelry.

These varieties of quartz are not widespread. The Scotland cairngorm deposits of the Highlands are virtually depleted. Excellent smoky quartz comes from the Swiss Alps, Spain, and the Pikes Peak region of central Colorado.

CHALCEDONY

The term chalcedony embraces an extensive group of gems in a wide range of colors and with a bewildering array of names. All these stones have a *cryptocrystalline structure*, which means that they are fibrous (or partly granular). It is impossible to determine the structure without a microscope.

Unlike many of the varieties of crystalline quartz, the chalcedony gems are characteristically translucent or opaque rather than transparent. They have a compact appearance and a waxy luster, and occur most frequently in rounded and imitative forms or as cavity linings.

No single classification of the cryptocrystalline quartz gems has ever satisfied all mineralogists or jewelers. Several of the major varieties are much better known than the general name chalcedony, which is little used for any

212

particular stone. A convenient system of nomenclature that is gaining in favor puts only light-colored gray, blue, milky-white, and yellowish-brown stones that have no other special names under chalcedony proper and applies other names, such as agate and jasper, to the more significant colors and patterns. The distinction between the varieties of chalcedony is, in fact, based almost exclusively upon color and pattern, a reminder of the days when they were all regarded as quite different substances because they look dissimilar.

The chalcedony gems have been the chief medium for engraving since the beginning of that art. The current popularity of amateur gem cutting in America affects this group of stones far more than any other, because they are so abundant, inexpensive, and varied, and can be worked without too much difficulty, yet offer the lapidary a reasonable degree of hardness. The prevailing mode of cutting is cabochon, but carved objects of all sorts, from spheres and transparencies to simple ornaments and intricate novelties, are made from chalcedony.

Carnelian

Red chalcedony, varying in hue from pink to blood red and from honey yellow to orange, and colored by ferric iron oxide, is called *carnelian* or *cornelian*. No other gem has been carved into so many seals and signet stones, and carnelian beads have been popular for centuries. The smooth, lustrous polish that carnelian takes is one of its chief delights. Noted sources are India and Brazil, and good stones have come from Tampa Bay in Florida.

Sard

When the color of chalcedony approaches brown, carnelian grades into sard, which is just as well known by name, although the Biblical references to this gem probably referred to the true red carnelian. Sard was worked also by ancient and Renaissance craftsmen.

Chrysoprase

Apple-green chalcedony, nicely colored by nickel oxide, was once considered the most beautiful variety. The name for it, chrysoprase, is derived from the Greek words meaning "golden green." After the exhaustion of the deposits in Silesia, over a hundred years ago, this gem became rare and consequently was extensively imitated. Rather recent discoveries of chrysoprase in California and Oregon have helped to restore the genuine material to public attention.

Prase

Although some prase is clear crystalline quartz containing many green fibers of the mineral called actinolite, the name prase is also applied to chalcedony the color of which, like that of chrysoprase. is green. Prase, however, is more like sage green and is duller in tone. The best stones have come from Saxony, Germany.

Plasma

A gem similar to prase, but often bright grass green in color, is called plasma. A frequent characteristic of this stone is the presence of white or yellow spots on the green background.

Bloodstone

The combination of red and green in one gem gives us bloodstone. Irregular spots of red, resembling drops of blood, against an otherwise solid body of dark green, make this one of the really unusual stones. Remarkable portrayals of the Crucifixion have been carved in bloodstone, and it serves well in men's signet rings. Another name for the gem, common in Britain but not in America, is *heliotrope*. India furnishes the best bloodstone, and other fine specimens come from the Ural Mountains.

Jasper

Almost any color may mark the presence of jasper, for this general name is applied to the deeply colored varieties of chalcedony which are virtually opaque because of an excess of coloring matter. Such impurities are usually red, brown, yellow, or green and are due mostly to iron oxides which appear in patches or bands. The name *ribbon jasper* identifies a stone with broad varicolored stripes. *Egyptian jasper* has yellow or brown zones. Some interesting rocks known as conglomerates contain rounded or angular boulders of jasper. In spite of its commonness, jasper has been carved into a number of rather valuable

215

art objects, particularly in Russia, where Siberian material with alternating red and green stripes has been much used.

Moss Agate

Although moss agate does not contain any moss, either plant or fossil, it preserves an eternal landscape in stone.

Fig. 95   Typical Moss Agate from Yellowstone River, Montana

(See Fig. 95.)   The fascination found in these intricately branching designs is hard to surpass in the whole realm of gemology.   Realistic scenes of mountain and lake, coast and forest, park and stream suddenly spring into view as the lapidary removes the outer layer or "skin" and moistens the stone.   Mineral matter, usually manganese oxide or sometimes iron oxide, spreads out to form dendritic or treelike patterns in this variety of chalcedony.   The prevailing color is black or brown, but sometimes the impurity consists of fibers of chlorite which present a tangle of green

216

resembling seaweed; sometimes moss agate shows a splurge of spectacular colors.

The great variety of designs to be found in agates of this sort has given rise to an equal variety of names. Gems from India are called *Mocha stone*. Terms such as *flower agate, plume agate, scenic agate, landscape agate, seaweed agate,* and *tree agate* are representative of the almost countless descriptive and local names that are current in one place or another. As is true of most of the varieties of chalcedony, American moss agate is found in its greatest profusion in the western states; Montana, along the Yellowstone River (Fig. 95), and Wyoming, along the Sweetwater River, are the most noted. Miniatures carved from American moss agate are shown in Fig. 53.

Agate

The term agate may include the moss agates just described as well as chalcedony in which the color is distributed in irregular patches, as in many of the well-known *thunder egg* nodules (Fig. 96) of Oregon and California. But the proper use of the word agate is restricted to chalcedony in which the colors are laid out in wavy concentric bands which conform to the cavity of the volcanic rock in which the silica was originally deposited. Constant or recurrent changes in the nature or degree of the impurities that produce the coloring matter are reflected in the successive layers as they build up the stone. The bands may differ in thickness or they may be fairly uniform for a considerable distance. An infinite variety of patterns and colors is the result; see Fig. 97.

217

Interesting names are given to these variants according to the design, which often depends solely upon the direction in which the stone is cut. If, for example, a rounded specimen is sectioned across the layers, a face of the stone

Fig. 96   Oregon Thunder Egg
Sawed and polished specimen partly filled with agate.

may show complete rings surrounding a solid center, like a target; such a piece is called an *eye agate*. *Fortification agate* (Fig. 98) has angular bands whose outline imitates the ground plan of a fort. *Iris agate* appears colorless until held in the proper direction toward the light, when suddenly a swirl of rainbow colors comes into view, owing to the diffraction of light from extremely closely spaced

218

parallel layers. The term *banded agate* is more or less redundant, if the limited definition of agate is accepted. The word agate itself came from the river Achates (now the Drillo) in Sicily, along the banks of which the earliest stones were found.

The town of Idar-Oberstein in Germany was once noted

Fig. 97 Polished Agates Showing Growth Structures
Top specimen, Brazil; lower specimens, Wyoming and South Dakota. [Rushmore Museum.]

for the finely colored agates found in the vicinity. The skill that the inhabitants acquired in cutting them for the trade was soon applied to other kinds of stones and they developed the world's largest gem-cutting industry. As the local deposits of agate diminished, some of the lapidaries moved elsewhere. A few of the emigrants went to South America, where they became acquainted with the vast quantity of pale agates in Uruguay and southern Brazil. These were sent back to Germany for cutting, and from the newly discovered and apparently limitless source of

219

supply came the impetus to experiment with artificial methods of enriching the color on a commercial scale.

The natural colors of few agates compare in vividness
with those obtained by soaking the stones in certain chemi-

Fig. 98   Superb Fortification Agate

cals, and one may safely assume that any brightly colored
agate has been thus treated. The principle underlying this
process is that the layers of silica that constitute agate are
porous in varying degrees, so that some layers take up
certain coloring matter while other layers remain un-
affected by the same chemical. After years of experimentation a fairly standard sequence of treatment has evolved,

although each sample has to be tested to determine its possibilities. During World War II, when German products were unavailable, agates from hundreds of domestic localities were examined by American dealers with the discovery of only a few stones that proved to be susceptible to systematic improvement in color.

Besides agate, other varieties of porous chalcedony may be stained attractive colors, but the chief result has been to simulate some more popular gem. Perhaps the most important examples of such artifice are the production of green "chrysoprase" from agate or ordinary chalcedony and of blue "lapis lazuli" from jasper.

Onyx

When the layers of agate are straight, parallel, reasonably wide, and of conspicuously contrasting colors, the term onyx is properly used. The sharply defined colors provide the gem engraver with a most suitable medium for cameos with a head of one color on a background of another. Modern cameos are carved largely in stained chalcedony, but the natural colors of many ancient gems are satisfyingly rich. The most typical arrangement consists of a white head against a black field. The word onyx is often used to refer merely to black chalcedony, which has for centuries been produced by soaking the stone in honey or in a sugar solution and then charring the sugar with sulfuric acid; a superior new process, employing cobalt nitrate and ammonium sulfocyanide, was described by George O. Wild in 1947. True onyx, however, is chalcedony of more than one color.

221

Sardonyx

Sardonyx is therefore onyx having a combination of sard (or its more reddish cousin, carnelian) and chalcedony of another color, usually white or black. It too is a popular stone for cameos.

Petrified Wood

Wood turns to stone—even to gemstone—when silica-bearing waters, percolating through the ground or rising from cooling bodies of rock below, reach a place where trees have been submerged and preserved from decay and deposit their mineral matter in the cells of the trunks, branches, and twigs. In the process they usually replace the woody substance and carry it away but preserve the plant structure, often with such remarkable fidelity that the species of tree can be identified.

Although many minerals replace wood, by far the most abundant replacement is chalcedony. Hence the term petrified wood is virtually synonymous with *silicified wood*. *Opalized wood* is the same product if the silica is present as the opaline mixture of cristobalite and water. Petrified wood so frequently exhibits regular banding or the swirling patterns of cloudy agate that the name *agatized wood* is very appropriate. Large patches of bright colors give the name *jasperized wood*.

Petrified forests and smaller areas of petrified wood are rather widely distributed, though much less so than the profusion of original timber suggests. Each deposit has its own characteristic features such as the kind of tree, the

222

range of size of the logs and limbs, the state of preservation, the presence or absence of bark, and the colors.

Petrified Forest National Park and the adjacent areas in Arizona have furnished the major part of the world's silicified wood for gem purposes. Reddish-brown, cherry-red, and black colors are the most distinctive. The stone trees lie at random over a large region, as if they had once been driftwood.

Petrified wood is found to some extent throughout the American West. The small black and white limbs and twigs from Eden Valley, Wyoming, and the handsome specimens from the Cycad Forest National Monument in the Black Hills of South Dakota are surely outstanding. The central and the eastern states yield petrified wood from a number of localities, the oldest in geologic time being in the Catskills of New York. Excellent petrified wood is found also in Canada, in Patagonia, and elsewhere.

Besides these gems and ornamental stones, some of which also have their everyday industrial uses, quartz and chalcedony include other materials deserving mention for their extensive commercial applications.

Sand, which is usually composed almost entirely of quartz grains, is used in the manufacture of glass and cement and as an abrasive and flux. *Gravel*, consisting of coarser fragments of quartz, is used in road construction. Natural aggregates of quartz in the form of *sandstone* (a sedimentary rock) and *quartzite* (a metamorphic rock) constitute important building and paving stones. *Itacolumite* is a curiously flexible sandstone—"the rock that bends"—found in India and North Carolina and associated with diamond in Brazil. *Flint*, a form of chalcedony quartz

223

having a conchoidal fracture, was vital to primitive man for his weapons and implements and later as a means of striking fire.

OPAL

Opal is unique in the gem kingdom. It has little color of its own, yet shines forth in the radiant splendor of all the other gems, combining the reddest red, the bluest blue, the greenest green, and every possible hue in its purest quality. Because the colors of opal are due to the interference of light rays, rather than to the absorption of a part of white light, they are of spectral purity and intensity. Ruskin wrote that opal "shows the most glorious colors to be seen in the world, save only those of clouds." In Roman times opal was, next to emerald, the most valuable gem, and the naturalist Pliny related that Mark Antony exiled a wealthy senator, Nonius, because he refused to sell an opal the size of a hazel nut. The name of the gem comes from the Sanskrit word meaning "precious stone."

The enthusiasm which opal arouses in artists and poets is not too extravagant. Opal is probably the most difficult of all gems to describe adequately to someone who has never seen a specimen, especially since there are several varieties of precious opal, conspicuously different from each other. All of these share an unsurpassed play of color as their chief mark of distinction.

White opal scintillates against a solid background, which is always light, either white or tinted some pale color. *Black opal*, on the contrary, has a dark background—seldom really black but usually blue or gray—which serves as a perfect foil for the colors superimposed on it. *Fire opal* is rather transparent and has a red, orange, or yellow body color against which some opalescence is displayed. *Common opal* includes the many kinds of opal that lack a play of color.

Opal is a mineral but it is a mixture of water and a silica mineral called cristobalite, having only a slight regularity in its internal structure. Hence it is not found in crystals but prefers to grow in irregular and imitative shapes, which often fill cavities in rock, coat surfaces of other minerals, or even replace the other minerals.

In composition opal is hydrous silica; its content of water ranges generally from 6 to 10 per cent in precious opal, and to 21 per cent in common opal. The opal material is deposited as a jelly from natural hot waters or hot springs. As it cools it hardens and loses part of its original water. This solidification produces cracks, which may become filled with other opal material. When the new opal contains even a slightly different amount of water it has a different refractive index. Within the stone layers are built up which reflect the light rays in such a way that they interfere. (The same interference causes the colors of soap bubbles.) The particular color that is obtained depends upon the thickness and uniformity of the layers and the direction in which they are viewed. The effect produced by the interference of light rays is often called "fire," but the term should be restricted to dispersion.

Opal must be handled with care. Besides being rather brittle it is not especially hard. Furthermore, it absorbs ink and grease; conversely, it may lose water and disintegrate. Heat, even more than dryness, is its dangerous enemy.

White Opal

The *precious opal* of the ancients was white opal. It is often referred to as *Hungarian opal* because of the source of the Roman gems, as well as of many in our own times. The actual locality is at Marmaros in the Nagy Banya district of present Czechoslovakia; the usual reference is to Czernowitz, but that town (spelled variously) is about 200 miles from the mines and is really the marketing and cutting center.

The light background of white opal may actually be yellow, pink, or some other light color, according to the impurities that were picked up by the silica. Since opal may show any hue, special names are given to stones characterized by certain colors or patterns. *Harlequin opal* has even patches of color like a mosaic. *Lechosos opal* has a deep-green play of color.

In 1889 the rich opal deposits of the continent of Australia were brought to public attention when a hunter picked up a fine specimen while he was trailing a wounded kangaroo. This place became known as White Cliffs and is in New South Wales. In 1915 the Coober Peby or Stuarts Range field in South Australia began to supply choice white opal. A minor source of white opal is Honduras.

Black Opal

A superior black opal should not be ranked below any other gem. The "smothered mass of hidden fire" that flashes from it shows more wonderfully because of the dark background, as fireworks or meteors appear to best advantage at night. Black opal that is actually black is exceedingly rare; the typical color is dark blue or gray, depending upon the impurities, of which iron is the most important.

Black opal was unknown until the discovery in 1903 of the fabulous Lightning Ridge field in New South Wales,

Fig. 99   Rainbow Ridge Opal Mine, Virgin Valley, Nevada

Australia.   Other discoveries near by and in adjacent Queensland followed.   A find of black opal in Humboldt County, Nevada, made the United States an opal producer. Among the fine gems taken from that field is the magnificent Roebling opal now in the United States National Museum in Washington.   The mine that furnished it is shown in Fig. 99.   Unfortunately, Nevada opals often develop a multitude of fine cracks upon exposure to the atmosphere.

The occurrence of the Australian and American black opal is very different from that of the Hungarian stones. Some of the best material is found in organic remains, replacing fossil wood, shells of former sea animals, and bones of extinct reptiles that inhabited the land geologic ages ago. The tendency of black opal, particularly, to be deposited in very thin seams makes it often necessary to include a piece of the country rock in the finished gem to provide a substantial support; such stones are called *opal-matrix*. *Opal doublets*, which have a thin slice of opal cemented to a backing of plain opal, black chalcedony, or glass, are fairly common in good jewelry.

The current scarcity of black opal marks the end of another cycle in the fortunes of this gem. Once highly prized, it fell into disfavor after the publication of a novel by Sir Walter Scott in which an enchanted opal was the cause of tragedy. Queen Victoria revived the popularity of opals by bestowing them as wedding gifts and thereby aided the development of the newly opened Australian mines. Now the deposits "down under" are nearing depletion; we are left with the discouraging thought that, except as family heirlooms and museum pieces, this glorious gem may soon become only a memory.

Fire Opal

Owing to its transparency, fire opal is the only variety of opal that may be appropriately faceted. At its finest it is only slightly milky. The play of color is usually hidden deep within the stone, disguised by the overall red to yellow color. A combination of red opalescence and red background is most desired. The mines near Querétaro and elsewhere in Mexico are the major source of fire opal, though some has been reported from Asia Minor.

Common Opal

A transition from precious opal with its play of color to common opal without any play of color is exemplified by *hydrophane*, which sometimes shows opalescence only after it has been immersed in water.

Many of the other varieties of common opal resemble chalcedony and bear similar names. Thus *prase opal* is green, *jasper opal* is brownish, *agate opal* is banded, and *moss opal* has dendritic mosslike inclusions. Other varieties also have descriptive names, such as *resin opal* which has a resinous luster, and *rose opal* which is pink. *Cachalong* is a curious opal considered valuable in the Orient; it is so porous that it adheres to the tongue. *Hyalite* is clear and glassy. Better known to geologists are *geyserite* or *siliceous sinter*, which is common opal deposited by hot springs and geysers; and *tripolite* or *diatomaceous earth*, a chalky material formed in the sea from the shells of diatoms, a kind of algae.

NATURAL GLASS

Faceted gems of pleasing color but little value have been cut from three types of natural glass found at the surface of the earth.

Obsidian

Obsidian is the chief of these natural glasses. It is the result of the very rapid cooling of a volcanic lava, which would have formed granite or a related rock if it had solidified within the crust instead of flowing out upon

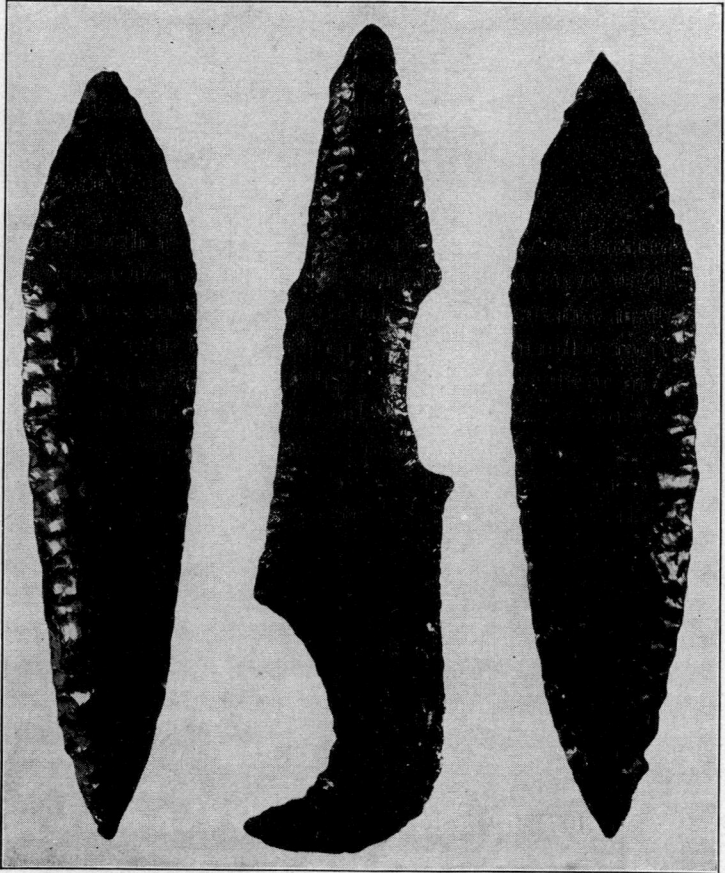

Fig. 100   Aztec Obsidian Blades, Mexico

[Middle American Research Institute.]

the ground. Obsidian closely resembles artificial glass and breaks with a similar conchoidal fracture (Fig. 51) and sharp edges; these qualities made it a necessity to ancient peoples, who used it for knives, arrowheads, mirrors, and countless other everyday objects. Blades of Aztec manufacture are shown in Fig. 100. Obsidian of many colors has been found, but most of the faceted gems have been cut from green specimens, whereas darker pieces are usually cut with rounded surfaces. A glass, obsidian is amorphous, of no definite internal structure. Its chemical composition is likewise variable but always high in silica. Obsidian is common in volcanic regions; such localities include Nevada, California, Arizona, Yellowstone National Park, several Mediterranean islands, Mexico, Iceland, and Greece.

Silica-Glass

A kind of natural glass, called silica-glass because it contains almost 98 per cent of silica, was discovered in the Libyan Desert in Africa in 1932. It had evidently been worked in sundry ways by the craftsmen of some prehistoric race. Large transparent, light yellowish-green pieces have been found. Their origin is a mystery, and only a fall from the sky seems an adequate explanation.

Tektite

The tektites are very curious natural glasses, which are known by several local and regional names according to the places in which they are found. Of these, *moldavite* from Bohemia and Moldavia is the best known and has long furnished transparent green gems sold as "bottle stone." Other sources are Australia, Borneo, and elsewhere within a single narrow zone that crosses the earth. Because they do not occur in association with volcanoes, like the volcanic glass obsidian, and their peculiar surface markings and rounded shapes suggest a prolonged whirling motion through the air, an origin outside our own planet has been proposed.

Chapter 6

Gems with a Genealogy

The four gems—pearl, coral, amber, and jet—which trace their ancestry to living things are not truly minerals, inasmuch as they have originated through organic activities of nature. Nevertheless, the first two contain mineral matter, and the constitution of the other two lies not far outside the scope of mineralogy. Surely all of them must be considered gems and deserve our serious attention. Among them they divide the earth, for two are gems of the sea and have an animal origin, whereas the other two are gems of the land and are derived from vegetation. The mysterious processes of life that have given rise to these gems make them more remarkable than the gems that have come to us from the depths of the earth or the outer vastness of cosmic space.

PEARL

The Queen of Gems rules supreme amidst the rich treasures of Neptune's domain. She has had no rival for her throne since the early day when she was first revealed to the race of men in her pristine beauty. Adorned only with a natural lustrous covering and needing no preparation or treatment, except perhaps to be drilled for stringing, pearl has excited the admiration and aroused the avarice of men, no less than of women, for millennia. Though the pearls of the ancients have not survived, as have the more durable mineral gems, their poets and writers have recorded in imperishable words their love of this gem.

Illumined by an iridescent surface, pearl presents a wide array of delicate tints, from the purest silvery white through light green, rosy pink, and creamy or golden yellow, to a shimmering black. Pearl thus serves most effectively as a foil for the bright reflection and intense fire of diamond and as a frame to enhance almost any kind of gem. As a row of individual gems, however, pearl is most highly regarded, for its beauty is sufficient in itself. For a gem of symmetrically spherical outline, translucent, with a rich but subdued sheen, and free from blemishes, "pearl of great price" has literal significance.

Pearl is a gem but not a gemstone. It is formed within the interior of certain *mollusks* which secrete the pearl-substance to line the shells in which they live. These mollusks, or shellfishes, are invertebrate animals which remove calcium carbonate from the water and with it build their shells. Inside the shell, enveloping the soft parts of the body, is a *mantle* which has cells that secrete both organic and mineral matter. The organic product of the mantle is called *conchiolin,* a brown substance related to the chitin of which our fingernails are made. The mineral product, derived from the sea, consists mainly of two crystalline forms of calcium carbonate, *calcite* (hexagonal) and *aragonite* (orthorhombic).

The shell is constructed in three layers, growing continuously and at the same time, but secreted in a regular order. The outer layer, deposited first, consists of conchiolin; the middle layer consists of tiny prisms of calcite cemented with conchiolin, and the inner layer consists of overlapping flakes of aragonite also cemented with conchiolin. This last layer is iridescent and is known as *nacre* or *mother-of-pearl;* as an ornamental material for buttons, implement handles, and inlaying it is well known.

The immediate cause of pearl formation is an irritation, resulting from disease or the introduction of a parasite or a foreign particle such as a grain of sand or piece of broken shell. To allay the discomfort the mollusk, through its mantle, secretes its customary products to seal off the intrusion. These products are built up in concentric layers like an onion, in reverse order from the arrangement in the shell—the zone of conchiolin being deposited first around the uninvited object and later surrounded by the two mineral zones to complete the pearl. The outer surface of pearl therefore corresponds to the mother-of-pearl layer of the shell.

To assume the ideal round form, a pearl must, of course, have been loosely held among the soft parts, the tissue or muscles, of the mollusk. If, however, a boring parasite has penetrated beyond the mantle and into the shell of the animal, nacreous material is deposited at that spot, and an irregular hollow pearl, known as a *blister pearl,* is formed. A solid pearl of any irregular shape is called a *baroque pearl* and may have been produced by the deposition of nacreous material against a fragment of some rough object, such as a bit of wood, or by other means unfavorable to symmetrical growth. A pearl may become

235

attached to the inside of the shell, in which case the pearly substance deposits only on the outer half, furnishing a hemisphere rounded on one side and flat on the other; such a gem is called a *button pearl* and is suitable for rings where only half of the pearl shows. Since a pearl may grow into almost any shape, many fanciful names are used in the trade. Round and pear-shaped pearls command the highest prices. *Seed pearls* are round ones weighing less than a quarter of a pearl-grain, and *dust pearls* are the most minute in size.

The texture of pearl is called its *skin*, and the luster is called its *orient*. Orient is due to the combined optical effects of interference of light from the thin curved layers near the surface and diffraction of light from the flaky layers of nacre that overlap one another. The rich orient, necessary to a valuable pearl, may be lacking when too much conchiolin is present. Traces of impurities in the water affect the color of pearl, and varying amounts of conchiolin give it a yellow to brown hue.

Of all gems, pearl is particularly susceptible to deterioration. The conchiolin, because it is organic, decays after a century or two. The calcium carbonate is immediately attacked by acids, even by perspiration. The moisture content gradually decreases in warm, dry climates, and a certain porosity allows for the absorption of grease and oil. Pearl, moreover, is not hard. Once scratched or stained, pearl cannot be permanently improved except by the uncertain procedure of peeling off the outer layers with a sharp blade.

Familiar enough is the newspaper story about the finding of a pearl in a restaurant oyster. It is true that the edible oyster does on occasion produce pearls, but the quality is

236

rarely good (especially after being cooked!) or the value more than nominal. The really precious pearl comes from various mollusks belonging to the same class but different genera. The shells may be single (univalve) or in pairs (bivalve). Two major types of pearl-bearing mollusks are recognized, according to whether they live in the ocean or in rivers. The salt-water pearl comes from the *pearl oyster*, whereas the fresh-water pearl comes from the *pearl mussel*. The pearl oyster includes a number of species of the genus Meleagrina, which provides the finest pearls and the best mother-of-pearl. Fresh-water pearls from inland streams are produced by mollusks of the genera Unio and Anodonta. In addition to these, other mollusks, including the clam, conch, and abalone, produce pearls.

Pearl fisheries encircle the globe. The product of each region is usually characterized by distinctive color, shape, or size that to an expert identifies the locality. Some species of mollusks are restricted to certain places but others are widely distributed. The unhappy experience which led the pearl mollusk to create in self-defense so wondrous an object is revealed in the distorted and stunted appearance of its shell. Such abnormal shells are eagerly sought and swiftly gathered in baskets by the divers, who remain about one minute at each descent.

The Arabian coast of the Persian Gulf has been a leading fishery since the Macedonians worked its oyster beds over 2,000 years ago. Another source of pearl for the ancients, in the Gulf of Mannar off the northwest shore of Ceylon, is also still important. The fisheries of the northern and western shores of Australia are noted, not only for their yield of pearl and mother-of-pearl, but also for the modern methods that are employed, including the

237

use of diving suits. Other productive localities are the Sulu Sea northeast of Borneo; the shores of the Aru Islands southwest of New Guinea; the lagoons and outer waters of scattered South Pacific coral islands and atolls; the Gulf of Mexico, the Caribbean Sea, and the western coast of Central and South America.

River pearls are taken from streams in several parts of Europe and America and in China and Japan. The most famous are those from Scotland, Wales, and Ireland, but by far the most productive fisheries are in the Mississippi and its tributaries, where systematic collecting has been done on a small scale each summer for many years.

The pearls found in Chinese river mussels furnished the inspiration for the experiments in artificially inducing pearl growth that led, seven centuries later, to the production of the cultured pearl, described in the chapter on "Man-Made Gems."

CORAL

When coral is considered an animal skeleton—for such it is—its romantic appeal may be regarded skeptically. Nevertheless, precious red or pink coral has been highly prized as a gem since ancient times and still is thought of as having a loveliness of its own, not dazzling or glowing, but quietly pleasing. In remote parts of the earth coral constitutes a source of wealth and is used for ornamenting clothing, jewelry, and valued articles of many kinds. Although found chiefly in the Mediterranean, coral was so much in demand in India during Roman days that there was little left for the inhabitants of the places that produced it. Good specimens of red color were widely used in China for the hat buttons that distinguished mandarins from other public officials. Coral contrasts so well with the blue and green hues of turquoise that in the mountainous parts of central Asia the two gems are worn together. At present coral is most popular in Italy, where the people have a near-monopoly of the fisheries and the manufacturing, turning the newly found coral into beads and sundry decorative items, often of curious shapes.

Fig. 101   Corals

A, modern coral colony, showing relation of living polyps (*a–d*) to stony skeleton (*e*). *B*, common type of ancient coral. [From Schuchert and Dunbar *Textbook of Geology*, 4th edition, copyright 1941.]

Only an excessively small part of the world's coral can be classed as gem material. *Common coral* of the reef-forming type covers vast areas of the warm oceans, and *fossil coral* is distributed in many regions where the climate in past geologic ages was favorable. Coral is created by tiny marine animals called *polyps*, which live in branching colonies (Fig. 101) that gradually extend themselves in size as new polyps grow. These organisms remove calcium carbonate from the water, deposit it in their tissues as crystallized calcite, and use it to build their skeletons,

239

which they leave to accumulate when they die. Impurities in the mineral matter give coral its color.

Gem coral is dredged mostly from shallow waters but may be found in depths to 1,000 feet. Besides the borders of the Mediterranean and around the larger islands, precious coral is secured in the Atlantic Ocean off Africa and Ireland, in the Pacific Ocean off Japan and Australia, and in the Persian Gulf. From the two latter seas the unusual *black coral* is obtained. It now comes from Hawaii also.

AMBER

Ancient in its use as a gem and even more in its origin, amber occupies an eminent place in gemology. There is no such thing as "new" amber. All of it began 10 million or more years ago, in what geologists call the Tertiary Period, when extensive forests of conifers grew along the Baltic coast in a warm climate very unlike that of the present day. Amber is the yellow resin—now hardened and fossilized into irregular lumps—that oozed from one species of tree, a pine called *Pinus succinifera*. The drops of resin remained on the ground while the trees decayed and were covered by invading seas; the forests were then buried by later sediments which incorporated the amber reworked from the previous deposits. The great glaciers of the Ice Age subsequently ploughed through this region, distributing some of the amber southward. Even now the Baltic Sea beating on the shore plucks loose the weakly consolidated rock and claims the amber in it for its own. Pieces are washed up on coasts as distant as England.

From these soft beds, called *blue earth*, comes the bulk of the world's amber. Until a century ago amber was

240

gathered from among seaweed at low tide. It has since been recovered in large quantities by open-pit mining. The center of production is on the peninsula of Samland in East Prussia, northwest of Königsberg.

Amber from northern Europe was marketed by the Phoenicians, who made it known to all the Mediterranean nations. Elaborate trade routes have traced the distribution of Baltic amber, which was the principal article of commerce between northern and southern Europe when amber beads served as a medium of exchange.

One of the most significant properties of amber, its ability to become negatively electrified by friction and to pick up tiny bits of various materials after being rubbed, was well known to the Greeks; from their name for the substance, *elektron*, is derived our word *electricity*. The word amber itself is Arabic.

Even more interesting than its electrical nonconductivity is the presence in many pieces of amber of a fascinating exhibit of entombed insects. As the sticky fluid exuded from the trees, it ran down the bark and caught within its fatal grasp any creature attracted to its sweet odor and any light object blown against it by the wind, and these were covered by the next flow of resin. Hundreds of kinds of insects—spiders, flies, beetles, ants, and centipedes —and equally varied plant remains—have been preserved with extraordinary fidelity, even to the tiniest antenna or finest cell pattern. (See Fig. 102.) As may be expected, some of the insects are only slightly different from those that plague us today, whereas others have become extinct. Much light is thrown on the fauna and flora of early times. Not only organic substances but almost any material con-

241

taminated the purity of amber. Alexander Pope wrote in
An Epistle to Dr. Arbuthnot:

> "Pretty! in amber to observe the forms
> Of hairs, or straws, or dirt, or grubs, or worms!
> The things we know are neither rich nor rare,
> But wonder how the devil they got there."

Amber of all hues of yellow, ranging from almost colorless to almost black, has long been carved into a multi-
plicity of ornamental articles. Beads, pipestems, and ciga-
rette holders are especially familiar. Prized in the art
collections of large museums are wonderfully executed
amber objects such as jewel cases, complete chess sets,
carved screens, statuettes, altars, and shrines.

Amber from the Baltic coast is properly referred to by
its mineralogical name, *succinite*. It is a hydrocarbon,
composed of hydrogen, oxygen, and carbon in variable
proportions, and represents a mixture of succinic acid,
several different resins, and a brown volatile oil called
amber oil. When boiled, amber deposits a black substance
called colophony or amber pitch, which is the principal
ingredient in the production of amber varnish.

There are several other varieties of amber differing
somewhat in composition from succinite. They are named
according to the locality from which they come.

Sicilian amber or *simetite* is the choicest and rarest, for
its yellow color may be tinged with a glorious red and
highlighted by a blue or green fluorescence that gives it
some of the beauty of opal. The gem, furthermore, is
usually clear and transparent, because it lacks the great
number of bubbles that so often make Baltic amber cloudy
and almost opaque.

Rumanian amber or *rumanite* is less well known than the others. It is characterized by many cracks and open spaces that give a curious glistening effect.

Burmese amber or *burmite* contains little or no succinic acid, as it belongs to the retinite group of resins. It comes

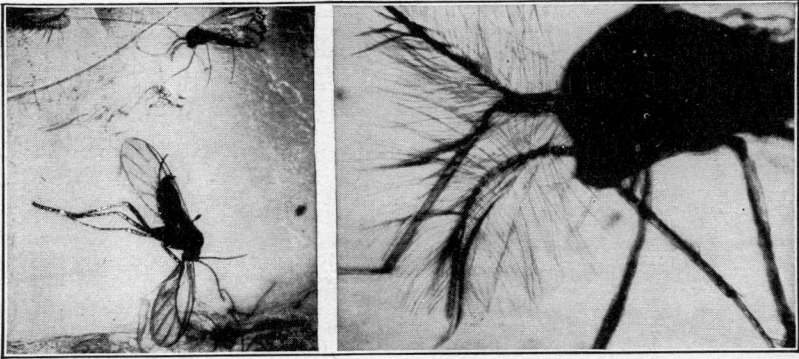

Fig. 102   Insects Preserved in Baltic Amber

Enlarged views showing the delicate detail. [From Schuchert and Dunbar *Textbook of Geology*, 4th edition, copyright 1941.]

from the Myitkyina district in Burma which also furnishes jadeite and is mined in primitive fashion and shipped mainly to China. Cracks filled with calcite too frequently mar the clarity of burmite.

As may be inferred from its recovery from the sea, amber is light enough to float in salt water; by this simple means it may be distinguished from glass and plastics (such as bakelite), which are the most common imitations. Amber is slightly too hard to be scratched by the fingernail, but it can be carved easily with a knife, drilled, and worked on a lathe. Amber is entirely amorphous, having

243

no crystal form or crystalline character. It will burn in a match or candle flame and gives off white fumes and an aromatic odor; the German name for amber, *bernstein*, means "stone that burns."

Because amber softens at a low temperature, small fragments of it are artificially compressed to form *ambroid* or *pressed amber*, which is then handled in the same way as the original material or extruded in the shape of rods. This product can scarcely be called an imitation but may be considered *reconstructed amber*.

Other natural resins besides amber serve similar purposes. *Copal* is a fossil resin, though younger than amber, and comes mainly from Africa; *kauri gum* is a modern resin from New Zealand. Chemical tests are needed to differentiate between them and true amber.

Ambergris, the name of which is the source of the word amber, is in no way related to amber. Ambergris is a fatty concretion formed in the body of whales and found floating in the sea; it is used in perfumery.

JET

Although, like amber, it owes its origin to tree life, jet nevertheless has had a very different history, because the wood itself, rather than the resin, has been preserved and is used in jewelry. Jet is a black variety of *lignite*, a rank of coal intermediate between peat and anthracite. It is derived from ancient coniferous wood through compaction and decomposition. The choicest quality of jet is uniform in color and in texture, dense enough to take a lustrous polish like black velvet and tough enough to be turned on a lathe or carved with a knife. It has a conchoidal or shell-like surface when it is broken.

Small ornaments of jet have been recovered from caves of prehistoric peoples in several parts of Europe, and jet amulets have been found in Indian pueblos in the American Southwest. The chief places, however, that are identified with this material are England and Spain. Spanish jet is imported into England to help maintain an industry that antedates the Roman occupation. Bronze-age buttons, rings, and beads have been found in pits throughout the country. British jet is often referred to as *Whitby jet* from the town on the Yorkshire coast that serves as the center of mining and craftsmanship. Early residents of the monastery of Whitby Abbey had rosary beads and crosses made from the jet found in the vicinity.

The so-called *jet rock* near Whitby is a shale containing logs and irregular pieces of jet associated with fish scales as evidence that this land was once submerged by the sea. Loose fragments of jet broken off by the waves and washed back onto the shore were for a long time the only source of supply, but eventually it became necessary to dig pits and mines into the rock itself.

Jet is utilized chiefly for religious articles and mourning jewelry, which was more fashionable during the 19th century than now.

Although the derivation is obscure, the word jet comes from a place in Asia Minor called Gagas where it was first discovered.

Chapter 7

Man-Made Gems

Imitation seems to be one of the universal traits of the human race. The cave man probably amused himself between bear hunts by grunting and growling in the manner of his prey. When he had progressed to the state in which he attached a high value to inanimate things of beauty, he tried to prepare substitutes for them to make them more abundant.

The Egyptians were skillful in the manufacture of gems from various materials and their achievements may be seen in museum collections of ancient art. The Romans reproduced their favorite gem, pearl, in enormous quantities. Later fine glass imitations called *paste* became so popular in Europe that they were a fad among the wealthy. All these substitutes are rather easy to identify, as their appearance is the only similarity between them and natural gems.

Through the magic of modern chemistry, much more amazing gemstones are available in a fascinating array of colors at the nearest jewelry store. So faithful in appearance and perfect in form are these synthetic stones that only an expert can recognize them with certainty; indeed, their very size and perfection are often the surest clues to their origin, for they rival the famous gems of history, the treasures of emperors and queens and merchant princes.

In addition to genuine gems—those which are formed in the earth or sea by the processes of nature or which come from beyond our world—the gem kingdom includes five types of *artificial gems*. These may be classified as imitation, synthetic, composite, treated, and cultured.

An *imitation gem* is a substance which is wholly manufactured but contains no natural gem material, even though it is made to look like a real stone. A *synthetic gem* is entirely different because it is crystalline and has every property of the natural gem; it is distinguishable only by certain minor peculiarities of structure due to the mode of manufacture. A *composite gem* consists of several pieces assembled to make a single larger or seemingly more valuable stone; even if it often serves a useful purpose by providing increased surface hardness, its primary intent is generally to deceive. A *treated gem* is one the natural, original color of which has been improved in salability by the application of heat, chemicals, or radioactivity. A *cultured gem* is a pearl grown by man's deliberate intervention in the life of an oyster. In the discussion of man-made gems, too rigid an adherence to an arbitrary classification may bring needless confusion, because there are so many intermediate kinds and so many possible combinations. The chief characteristics of these five main types, however, will be described in this chapter.

247

A considerable number of minerals, including many of the gems, have been made synthetically in the laboratory. They have the same chemical composition as the natural minerals and are essentially the same in all other respects except their origin. Only the few that have an important industrial use are made commercially.

Though they may be made in almost every conceivable hue and every possible shade and tint, nearly all the synthetic gems are varieties of only three species—corundum, spinel, and beryl. The flaming red ruby and the celestial blue sapphire are the best-known members of the corundum family. Spinel, on the other hand, is rather an unfamiliar stone, rather similar to corundum; there are natural crystals of both in the same gem gravels of the Orient, and until recently distinction was seldom made between them. A large proportion of the unusual gem names that one encounters are really trade-marked names for either synthetic corundum or synthetic spinel. Dirigem, erinide, ultralite, emerada, rozircon, and others often sold as new genuine gems are varieties of one or the other. Some colors are more conveniently made in corundum and others in spinel. Synthetic rutile (Titania) has no natural counterpart, nor does synthetic strontium titanate (Fabulite). Synthetic beryl is as yet represented only by its choicest variety, the green emerald.

Reconstructed Gems

No gems were known to be made synthetically until about eighty years ago, when a jeweler became suspicious of some rubies that he had bought; upon examination he saw that they were unlike any others in his stock. They were traced to an obscure chemist in Geneva, Switzerland, who had made them by fusing together several small rubies at a high temperature. In spite of their bubbles and cracks, their odd shade of color, and their brittleness, these stones were an improvement over all previous artificial gems, and somewhat better ones that were made afterward secured a ready sale.

For this type alone the term *reconstructed* should be reserved. The word is still erroneously applied to modern synthetics, but should be used only for the gems that resulted from the fusion of actual rubies. No "reconstructed sapphire" has ever been produced, for the blue color does not persist under the required amount of heat.

Pressed amber, which consists of small fragments of amber fused into a plastic mass, may also, as far as origin is concerned, be regarded as a reconstructed gem.

Synthetic Corundum

If bits of stone could be made into a single piece by artificial means, why, it was reasoned, could not such gems be made more cheaply by combining directly the simple chemicals of which they are composed? So scientists took up the challenge and set to work to prepare in a laboratory the rare gems that required long ages to form within the earth.

Edmond Fremy, a French chemist, in collaboration with Charles Feil, was finally able in 1877 to produce some ruby crystals, but they were too small to be of much value and hardly better than the tiny flakes made by Marc Gaudin

249

as early as 1837 or the small colorless fragments made by Ebelman in 1847. When Fremy had to retire, his able young assistant, Auguste Verneuil, took up the problem. With a perseverance that refused to recognize failure he invented new equipment and devised new methods. Success was achieved in 1902, with the production of *synthetic ruby* of admirable beauty, perfection, and size.

Synthetic sapphire was produced in 1910, only after the elusive blue color had first been secured accidentally in an entirely different species, which was discovered to be spinel. Since then synthetics have been put on the market in a wide array of colors, and the end has not yet been reached. The outstanding recent accomplishment is the introduction by the Linde Air Products Company of *star ruby* and *star sapphire*, which were made available in commercial quantity in September 1947.

Verneuil's method is still used in the manufacture of the millions of carats of synthetic corundum and spinel that are made every year. The equipment, only slightly modified from the original for more economical operation, is shown in Fig. 103. It is in general an inverted blowpipe which creates a high-temperature flame by a mixture of oxygen and hydrogen. Aluminum oxide powder, ground to particles the size of 4-millionths of an inch and mixed with the proper coloring matter, is fed through a screen by cam action and drifts down a tube of oxygen. Meanwhile, a jet of hydrogen enters from the side, and at the point at which the two gases meet, a flame of over 3,750 degrees Fahrenheit is obtained. The powder melts and drops onto a rotating pedestal as a single pear-shaped crystal called a *boule*, several stages in the growth of which are shown in Fig. 104. Its sides are smooth and bright, whereas its top is usually irregular and represents an abortive attempt to form the hexagonal crystal faces typical of corundum. After cooling, it is removed from the furnace and split

Fig. 103   Verneuil Furnace for Manufacture of Synthetic Corundum

[Linde Air Products Co.]

lengthwise to ease the strain that seems to be present. Boules average several hundred carats in weight. They are cut by the same methods as genuine gems.

A colorless stone, called *synthetic white sapphire*, is made from pure aluminum oxide, free from the impurities that tend to darken it. As in the natural stone, chromium oxide is the coloring matter in synthetic ruby. A smaller amount of chromium gives the tint of pink sapphire. Titanium oxide causes the blue color of synthetic sapphire. Nickel oxide imparts a range of yellow colors. The orange

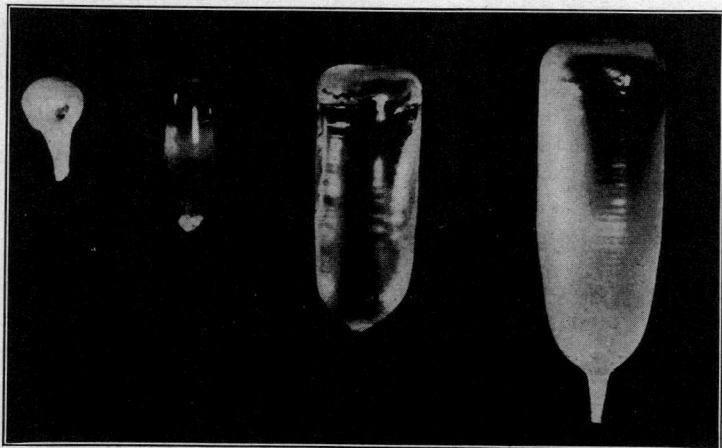

Fig. 104 Boules of Synthetic Corundum
[Linde Air Products Co.]

variety called *padparadschah* is seldom seen in natural corundum. A most unusual kind, colored by vanadium oxide, is wrongly called "synthetic alexandrite" because its color changes from green in daylight to red at night, as in the real gem, though the contrast of color is not nearly as distinct. It could not be synthetic alexandrite for it does not possess, except in appearance, the properties of chrysoberyl, of which true alexandrite is a variety. The addition of other metals to the vanadium yields other hues of green. Chromium and iron added to the titanium

252

of blue synthetic sapphire give a violet color. There is no commercial synthetic zircon or synthetic aquamarine, only synthetic corundum or synthetic spinel made in colors that are more or less appropriate.

These synthetic stones resemble the older imitations only in that both are man made. Otherwise they are so much like Nature's own gems that only a trained eye aided by a strong magnifying glass, sometimes even by a microscope, can determine which is the natural stone and which the manufactured one. They are alike in all important respects—hardness, specific gravity, refractive index, dispersion, and other properties which identify a gem. X-ray pictures show the structures to be precisely the same.

It happens, however, that the very process of making a synthetic stone leaves its "fingerprints," and the gem detective looks for these clues. The internal markings—bands of color and lines of structure—which are due to slightly variable conditions during growth are curved in synthetics, instead of being straight and angular as in genuine corundum. Synthetics contain round and oval gas bubbles, whereas the inclusions in genuine stones consist of actual crystals (as needles and in other shapes) of the minerals that occur in the earth with ruby and sapphire, and these inclusions have regular sides or intersect at exactly 60-degree angles. The kind and quality of the stone determines whether these intimate marks can be found with a hand lens or require a microscope. The bands of color in blue synthetic sapphire, for example, are more conspicuous than in the other varieties.

Because it is easier to cut synthetic-ruby boules without attempting to orient them, as is carefully done with most genuine rubies, the optic axis—the direction of single refraction—may lie in any position within the stone. Not only is the resulting color somewhat anomalous in comparison with that of a real ruby, but the twin dichroic colors of a synthetic are usually visible when a dichroscope is held against the top or table facet, whereas natural

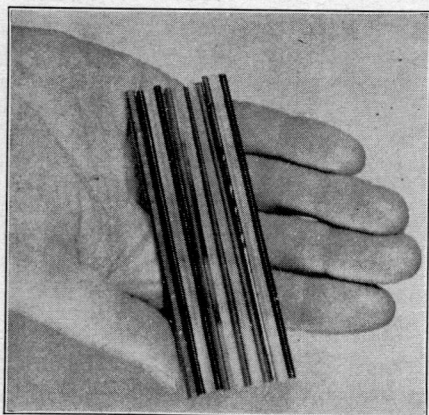

Fig. 105   New Rod Form of Synthetic Corundum
[Linde Air Products Co.]

ruby appears best when the table is perpendicular to the optic axis.

Apart from its use in jewelry, synthetic corundum plays a vital role in modern industry. Originally developed for instrument bearings, especially in watches and meters, it acquired new significance during the war, when an expanding technology found it valuable in equipment such as vacuum thermionic devices, diesel-engine injection nozzles, thread guides, oil-burner nozzles, and special abrasives. An entirely new use, which promises much for the future, is for gauges. A strand of nylon has recently been found to be the most effective polishing agent for the synthetic-corundum bearings in naval precision instruments, such as range finders.

When shipments from Switzerland, France, and Germany were threatened by the war, the Linde Air Products Company undertook in the autumn of 1940 to make synthetic corundum in the United States. Their factory opened in April 1942, and they claim to have made this country forever independent of foreign supplies. Another major triumph, previously attempted for 40 years in Europe without success, has been the manufacture of a new crystal form to supersede the familiar boule that is made for gems. By producing the corundum in long slender *rods*, shown in Fig. 105, several steps can be eliminated in the preparation of bearings. The boules must be split lengthwise to relieve stresses but the rods are annealed. Most of the material for industrial purposes is confined to the colorless variety, known in gemology as synthetic white sapphire.

Synthetic Spinel

In an attempt to secure a more even distribution of the difficult blue color in synthetic corundum, magnesium oxide was added as a flux. The resulting stone proved to be a different species, corresponding in composition to spinel. The boules, with square cross-section, show a more distinct crystal form than those of synthetic corundum, and they are isometric instead of hexagonal.

The most unusual feature about the composition of synthetic spinel is its excess of aluminum oxide. Most of the gems seem to have two or three times as much as is required

255

by the chemical formula, and thus they begin to approach the composition of corundum. This has its effect on the specific gravity and refractive index, which are thereby increased, although they seem to stay within the known range of natural spinel.

The blue stones are the most popular; those made to substitute for zircon and aquamarine are colored with cobalt oxide, as are those of the brilliant blue color that are sold simply as *blue spinel*, though their hue is quite unlike any natural spinel. A variety resembling alexandrite is produced, as in synthetic corundum, but the agents responsible for the peculiar changing color are chromium and cobalt, rather than vanadium. Synthetic spinel of many other colors, as well as colorless stones, are also made to satisfy the demands of the jewelry trade.

The internal structure of synthetic spinel is much clearer than that of its corundum counterpart and seldom shows either curved striations or gas bubbles.

Until World War II synthetic spinel was not used industrially except for gem purposes because its hardness, although considerable, is inferior to that of corundum, which costs no more to manufacture though more to cut. German wartime research, revealed in 1947 by the Office of Technical Services, succeeded in developing a process whereby synthetic spinel, after being cut into jewels for bearings, was hardened by heating.

Synthetic Beryl

To these two commercial species of synthetic gems, corundum and spinel, can now be added a third—beryl. Its wonderful *emerald* variety, since early times one of the most highly prized of all the gems, is now on the market in synthetic form.

Owing to the complexity of its chemical composition, in contrast to the much simpler corundum, attempts to synthesize emerald, or even to reconstruct it by fusing together pieces of actual beryl, had been attended by repeated failures. The result was always green glass instead of the required crystalline material. About 1934 two German chemists finally succeeded, though not by the Verneuil process, in making synthetic green beryl, to which they gave the name *igmerald*. In addition to having distinctive wisplike internal markings, it differed from most natural emerald in fluorescing red under ultraviolet light. Improved American gems, of good size and fine quality, have since become available, and future advances in manufacture seem likely to put synthetic emerald on a basis equal to synthetic ruby and sapphire in size and color. Prices are still high and the color does not equal that of the best natural emeralds but is better than the average.

Apart from their frequent fluorescence, the best means of identifying synthetic emerald is to observe the inclusions under high magnification. The black inclusions in the synthetics appear green, showing that they are a concentration of the coloring matter, which is chromium oxide, rather than the liquid bubbles found in genuine emeralds. Real emeralds, furthermore, contain carbon spots and tiny crystals of foreign minerals which are never present in synthetic stones.

The question is often asked why anyone would spend hundreds or thousands of dollars for a natural gem, when for a small part of that amount he can buy a stone which will deceive everyone except an expert. The answer is that much of the price of a real ruby or emerald lies in its rarity, and people will continue to pay the large sums that rare and beautiful things always command.

Synthetic Diamond

A lively interest has been maintained for a long while in the possibility of making synthetic diamonds. Apart from the prospect of drastic readjustments that might be faced by the jewelry business and the even more extensive benefits that should accrue to industry in general from an unlimited supply of its best abrasive, the remarkable optical, physical, and chemical properties of diamond would in themselves make its synthesis an achievement of extraordinary significance. To produce in a laboratory what is probably the most noteworthy substance of the inorganic world would indeed be a triumph of science.

All the older books on gems state that very small diamonds were made by Henri Moissan, a 1906 Nobel prize winner. His experiments were believed to have been successful, even though obviously not to a commercial extent. Carbon, which was obtained by burning sugar, was dissolved in molten iron, and upon being cooled quickly the metal exerted a tremendous internal pressure. The tiny particles that crystallized were assumed to be diamonds, but newer tests indicate that they were a carbide rather than a form of carbon. Other methods have been tried for many years by a number of competent workers, including several of the most distinguished scientists of recent times. German experts carried on extensive research during the war,

258

repeating Moissan's experiments and always with failure.

Diamond is deceivingly simple. In composition it is the only gem consisting of just one chemical element, carbon; it nevertheless defies the artificial reproduction of its single constituent. Carbon presents the difficulty of burning into a gas before it melts into a liquid. When it does crystallize, it is more likely to do so as its more stable form, the mineral graphite.

Most investigators have assumed that great pressure was the key to the production of diamond, and their equipment was designed chiefly to create it. Not until 1954 when the General Electric Research Laboratory applied both great heat (above 5,000 degrees Fahrenheit) and a pressure equivalent to a depth of 240 miles below the surface of the earth, was synthetic diamond first proved possible. The product is still only of industrial quality but improvements in size and clarity continue to be made.

IMITATION GEMS

Gilbert and Sullivan's Learned Judge, who wore "a ring that looked like a ruby," wasn't fooling himself, however much he might deceive others. He knew that the only similarity was a bright red color. All imitation gems resemble genuine ones solely in their superficial appearance, and, unlike synthetics, they may be identified with certainty by determining their optical or other physical properties. Although conspicuously inferior to synthetics in hardness, imitation stones frequently are as hard as some of the genuine stones which they are supposed to represent. Their chief advantage over synthetics lies in their even greater variety of color. Apart from the small synthetic beryl that is beginning to come into the market, the rich green of emerald, for example, can be obtained in no other homogeneous material, natural or otherwise, except glass. Some gems, particularly those showing curious optical effects, like opal and moonstone, cannot be made synthetically. The low cost of imitation gems is another advantage, for they are much less expensive to manufacture than synthetic crystals, and, before being polished, they are merely molded instead of cut.

Most imitation gems are made of *glass*. This versatile substance has been known for thousands of years, yet it is just entering upon its most promising era. Two main kinds of glass, crown and flint, are used for gems. Both consist mostly of silica obtained from sand; crown glass also contains calcium oxide (lime), and flint glass contains lead oxide. Metallic oxides and other chemicals are added to produce almost any desired shade or tint. Nontransparent glass, such as is used for imitations of opal and opaque gems, requires somewhat further treatment.

Because the ingredients may be mixed in almost any proportions, glass has a wide range of properties, though the types used for gems are fairly restricted. In rare cases glass may, usually by coincidence, have the same refractive index or specific gravity as a genuine gem of the same color. Two especially pure and constant kinds of glass are *fused quartz* (vitreous silica) and *beryl glass*, both of which are made by fusing the natural minerals into an amorphous mass; the chemical composition remains the same but the properties are changed.

Jewelers refer to the common glass imitations as *paste*, and the same material appears in the costume-jewelry advertisements of department stores under the term "simulated." A brilliant lead glass used to imitate diamond is called *strass*. A most distinctive and attractive gem is *goldstone*, copper crystals grown in glass. Imitation gems, as well as genuine ones, are often improved in brilliancy or color by foils, usually of metal, placed on their lower facets, or by coatings of mercury or pigment. *Rhinestones* and so-called *brilliants* are of this kind. Glass gems, being noncrystalline, may be distinguished from many genuine stones by their lack of double refraction and complete absence of dichroism, as well as by the presence of air bubbles and a measurable difference in properties.

Formerly concentrated almost exclusively in Czechoslovakia, the manufacture of glass imitations was introduced into the United States when imports from the occupied countries were halted during World War II. This infant American industry is at present struggling against the threat of cheap foreign competition. The molten glass, combined according to formula, with coloring matter added, is drawn into long rods called *canes;* one end of a cane is melted into a die of the desired shape. The better-quality stones are later polished. Hard glass is being developed that offers good prospects for the gem industry of the future.

Another imitation gem material, much more modern than glass but already useful in countless ways, comprises the group called the *plastics*. These are marketed under a variety of names, from the original celluloid to the familiar Bakelite and Catalin. Amber and jet, the two lightest gems, are imitated with particular effectiveness in plastics,

261

which like them have a resinous luster and a low specific gravity. Natural amber, however, is even lighter in weight than its man-made substitutes.

Other materials are used to a lesser extent. Imitation turquoise is commonly made these days by mixing various powdered substances. Ornamental stones may be imitated in *plaster*. *Stainless steel* containing chromium and nickel was rather widely sold a few years ago as "scientific hematite." The warrior-head intaglio design is stamped into the metal, producing a smoothly curved surface unlike the sharp lines of a hand-carved stone, and the characteristic red streak of true hematite is absent. Another important substitute for hematite is made of a ceramic material.

The best-quality imitation pearl dates back to 1656, when a Frenchman coated the inner side of a hollow sphere of opalescent glass with parchment sizing and applied to this sizing a preparation made from fish scales and called *pearl essence*. The rest of the interior was then filled with hot wax. This type of pearl is harder than the natural gem and of course has a glassy texture.

The average imitation pearl produced now, however, consists of a glass or plastic bead coated on the outside with pearl essence. The tendency of this material to peel is usually visible at the drill-hole.

A current post-war boom has developed among the Bay of Fundy fishermen, who find their catches of young herring worth far more for the silvery fish scales used in the manufacture of pearl essence than for food. Factories have been opened in Maine and Canada and probably elsewhere as well.

262

Two or more pieces assembled to make a single individual constitute a composite gem. *Doublets* (Figs. 106 and 108) contain two pieces and *triplets* (Figs. 107 and 109) contain three. These may be cemented or fused together, either before or after the cutting process. Composite gems

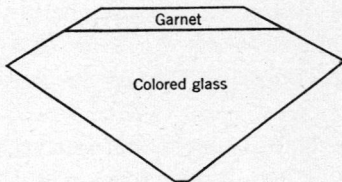

Fig. 106
Part-Garnet Doublet

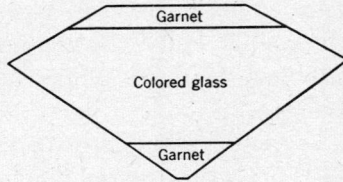

Fig. 107
Part-Garnet Triplet

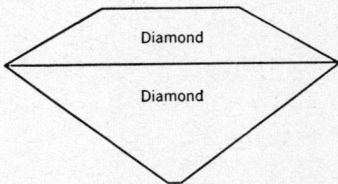

Fig. 108   Diamond Doublet

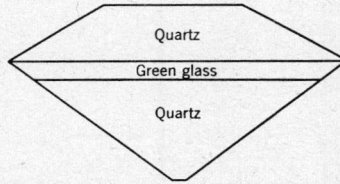

Fig. 109   Soudé Emerald

Composite Gems

may consist entirely of genuine stones, or of a combination of real and imitation materials. (All-glass composites, or glass with a foil back, can hardly be classed as anything but imitations.) Except the opal doublet and emerald triplet, composite gems are seldom made these days.

Older jewelry, however, contains them in abundance. They were originally designed to pass the hardness test, first by the addition of a hard top of a natural mineral, usually quartz or almandite garnet (Fig. 106), and later by similar protection of the bottom (Fig. 107). The development of synthetic corundum and spinel, with their superior hardness and wide choice of color, has made this arrangement unnecessary.

When the purpose is to combine several fragments of a genuine gem into one larger and consequently more valuable stone, only the natural material is used. Diamond doublets (Fig. 108) are on rare occasions made in this manner.

A familiar doublet involving precious black opal derives its value from the tendency of this exquisite gem to occur in layers of such thinness that they need to be supported in order to be mounted in jewelry. By cementing the opal slice onto a base of ordinary black opal or black chalcedony, the necessary strength is secured.

The most successful substitute for emerald is a triplet called *soudé emerald* (Fig. 109), consisting of a top and a base of quartz, enclosing between them, sandwich-like, a flat plate of green glass which furnishes the color. The quartz assures a reasonable degree of hardness and may show natural flaws resembling those of emerald. This substitute is important because the rich color of emerald has never been produced in synthetic corundum or spinel, with their superior durability, and synthetic beryl is made only in small specimens which have not yet entered the market in quantity.

The true nature of a composite gem becomes evident when the surface separating the parts can be seen. Because all stones assume the color of their back facets, any difference in color between the sections is visible when a gem is viewed sideways. Holding it over white paper or cloth and breathing upon it helps to reveal the plane of junction. The best way, especially when a stone has a uniform color throughout, is to immerse it in a highly refractive liquid. If a composite gem is cemented together, it may separate in boiling water, alcohol, or chloroform.

TREATED GEMS

Many gems can be altered in appearance, especially in color, by the application of *radioactivity*, *heat*, or *chemicals*. These agencies are, in fact, the ones that often naturally change the color of gems in the earth. Gems may be treated to meet the temporary whims of fashion, to improve the beauty of an inferior specimen, or to produce a distinctively different variety of a familiar gem. Although many kinds of gems are susceptible to treatment, only a few are systematically altered in the trade.

When exposed to the emanations of radium, diamond not only becomes radioactive but turns green. Other gems are affected by this phenomenon, but they are of little commercial value. Any green diamond offered for sale should be suspected of having been thus doctored, even though natural green diamonds are not excessively rare. The artificially induced color seems to remain permanently under normal conditions.

The practice of heating yellow Brazilian topaz to a delicate pink yields a gem that has long been a favorite in fashionable jewelry, but the production seems to have declined lately because of economic reasons rather than a change in fashion. A much more active industry in Brazil is the creation of citrine, ranging in hue from light yellow

265

to rich orange, by heating other varieties of quartz; crystals of amethyst give the best results, but uncut smoky quartz is more often used.

Zircon is, of all the gems, by far the most important from the standpoint of heat treatment. The most popular hues—blue, golden yellow, and colorless—are derived from brown zircon. The exclusion of air from the charcoal furnace gives rise to the blue variety; the presence of air results in the golden variety. Colorless zircon is obtained both ways.

Frequent attempts are made to improve the color of turquoise or restore the highly prized blue color after it has turned green. Few of them, however, are more than temporarily successful.

The staining and dyeing of agate and other varieties of chalcedony quartz are so significant, involving an entire industry, that discussion of the methods used has been reserved for the chapter "Gems of the Silica Group."

CULTURED PEARL

If not entirely man made, cultured pearls are at least man aided. Nature has been ably encouraged in her work of producing a lustrous gem from the misfortunes of a pearl oyster, which without interference might have lived comfortably and barrenly in the remoteness of the sea.

The cause of pearl formation was discovered as early as the 13th century, when the Chinese took advantage of their knowledge and forced small metal images of Buddha between the shell and the mantle of fresh-water pearl mussels. The images became coated with nacre and were later removed as pearls.

Somewhat over 60 years ago the Japanese, following a similar procedure, cemented a mother-of-pearl pellet to the inner lining of the shell and obtained a *blister pearl*, coated only on one side.

Further experimentation culminated in the production by the Japanese of completely round pearls, the appearance of which in quantity in 1921 created a panic in the markets of the world until it was learned how they could be distinguished from the entirely natural gem. To these pearls the term *cultured* is applied, though some unsuccessful attempts have been made to confine it to the older artificially stimulated partial pearl (the blister pearl) and to refer to the whole pearl as *cultivated*.

The equivalent of a surgical operation must be performed. A small bead made of mother-of-pearl is placed within a sac cut from the mantle of a three-year-old oyster, and the sac is then inserted in the tissues of another oyster, which covers it with nacre in the usual way during the succeeding seven years. At the end of that time the pearl appears as shown in Fig. 110. Both before and after they are treated, the mollusks are kept in cages suspended from rafts in the water and are repeatedly inspected by women divers (see Fig. 111) for signs of disease. Owing to the usual hazards and uncertainties of living things, the percentage of good-quality spherical pearls is small.

Under pressure of a war economy, the Japanese pearl "farms," including the newly established one which produced pink pearls in a fresh-water lake, were compelled to suspend operations. The industry has not only been re-established in Japan but it has expanded into Australian waters.

267

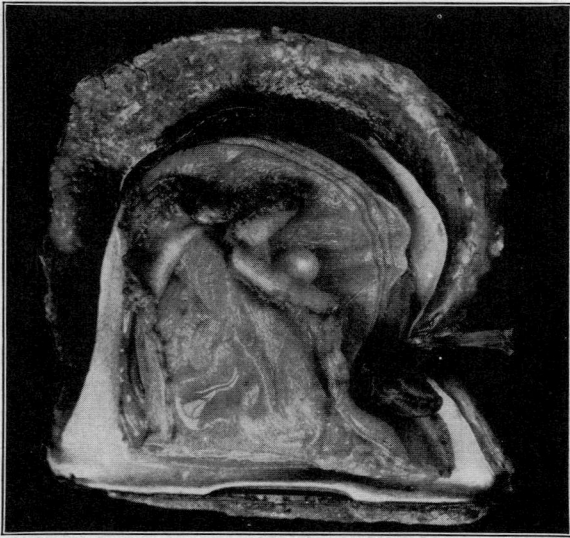

Fig. 110 Cultured Pearls after Seven Years' Growth

Fig. 111 Woman Diver Tending Cultured Pearl Oysters

When a mother-of-pearl bead serves as the nucleus of a cultured pearl, its presence makes possible several methods of distinguishing the product from a natural gem. A drilled pearl may be examined with an instrument called an endoscope, which concentrates a beam of light into the hole. The light follows the concentric structure of a wholly natural pearl and is reflected out of the opposite end of the drill-hole; but it is deflected by the core of a cultured pearl and comes to the surface of the pearl at a different point. For undrilled pearls X-rays and special microscopes are employed to determine their origin.

Chapter 8

Luminescent Gems

Few aspects of gemology have grown more in popular favor during recent years than the collection, display, and study of gems that glow in *ultraviolet light*. Because ultraviolet radiation is itself invisible, exposing such gems to it produces secondary colors that are not present in the original source of illumination. The gems glow or *fluoresce* in darkness that is complete, unless some extraneous reflection of ordinary light has not been filtered out. When a gem continues to glow even after the ultraviolet rays have been turned off, it is said to *phosphoresce*. Both fluorescence and phosphorescence are combined under the general term *luminescence*.

Neither of these effects is an exclusive response to ultraviolet radiation. Both may also be revealed by exposure to X-rays, cathode rays, or the emanations that result from radioactivity. These other methods sometimes produce a more intense luminescence than can be obtained from ultraviolet rays, but their use is greatly restricted because of expense, inconvenience, and danger. The development on a commercial scale of good sources of ultraviolet radi-

270

ation has made it the most useful means of observing fluorescence and phosphorescence.

Phosphorescence was studied before fluorescence. In 1602 an Italian shoemaker noticed that specimens of barite, a heavy mineral which he had collected for his spare-time practice of alchemy, shone in the dark after they had been in a strong light. Proof was afterward found that this mineral, as well as other substances that behaved in the same way, could not be merely storing up sunlight or light from a fire and giving it off again, inasmuch as the color of the light underwent a change.

The investigation of fluorescence led finally to the discovery of the underlying principles of both phenomena. A number of famous scientists, including Sir David Brewster, Sir John Herschel, and Sir George G. Stokes, worked on the problem. Stokes described the effect best and named it after the mineral fluorite, which often shows it. Much, of course, remains to be learned; even the real difference between fluorescence and phosphorescence is a matter of definition.

Ultraviolet rays are of exactly the same nature as visible light and travel at the same speed. Both belong to the vast range of electromagnetic radiation, of which white light and its component colors represent only an extremely small part, about intermediate between the long, slowly vibrating rays of wireless telegraphy and the very short, rapidly vibrating cosmic rays. As the wavelength of the radiation decreases and its frequency of vibration increases, the violet light of the visible spectrum gives way to the region that contains the invisible ultraviolet ("beyond the violet") rays.

In accordance with the observation that ultraviolet radiation on luminescent substances, including gems, gives rise to visible light, Stokes' law states that the resulting rays are always of longer wavelength than the primary rays. This law has since been disproved as a generalization, but it is usually correct. Another instance of the lengthening of rays is utilized in solar heating of homes; some of the visible sunlight that passes through the windows is changed into the longer infrared (heat) rays which are stopped by the glass and thus remain inside to heat the interior. Luminescent gems act as transformers of light and change the wavelength of rays as an electrical transformer changes a given voltage.

The analogy between the structure of atoms and the arrangement of our solar system—the sun and its planets, including the earth—is familiar. Electrons, which are particles carrying a negative electrical charge, are assumed to revolve in definite orbits or shells around a central nucleus that has a positive charge, as the planets revolve in their concentric orbits around the sun. The impact of ultraviolet radiation upon luminescent substances causes them to absorb the added energy by displacing electrons to orbits farther out. This unstable condition is corrected when the electrons return to their original positions; the excess energy is given off in the form of luminescence. For luminescence to take place, therefore, absorption of energy must first occur. Previous absorption of energy distinguishes phosphorescence of the kind referred to here from the familiar phosphorescence due to biochemical action, which results in the emission of light, often voluntarily, by fire-flies, glow-worms, certain fish, and other organisms.

Besides these types of luminescence, there are a number

272

of others, each with a special name. Luminescence may be produced by heat, friction, crystallization, cooling, and electrochemical action. *Ultraviolet* luminescence is the kind in which we are most interested.

As impurities in gems, often in the most minute traces, have a great influence on the color, so also they have a profound effect on the nature and intensity of the luminescence. Those impurities that cause luminescence are called *activators*, and those that prevent the effect are called *inhibitors*. This dependence upon small amounts of a foreign substance is a disadvantage in the identification of gems, because two stones of the same species but from different localities may fluoresce quite differently. It is an advantage, however, in classifying some gems according to origin, for some of the fluorescent colors in different localities are distinctive.

The difference between fluorescence and phosphorescence depends on the speed with which the electrons return to their previous positions. In fluorescence the electrons return immediately to their stable positions. Phosphorescence requires that they come back to normal in two stages, causing a delay in the disappearance of the light. Some gems flare for hours after the ultraviolet light has been turned off and may even brighten the corner of a room by their intense glow.

The interest of American mineral collectors in the subject of luminescence started with discoveries in connection with *willemite* from Franklin, New Jersey. Only a relatively few specimens have ever qualified as gems, but they have been attractive ones, and the value of willemite as an ore of zinc has alone been great enough to make it significant among minerals. A fortuitous discovery was made by men working in the mine that the willemite could be distinguished from its associates (mostly franklinite, zincite, and calcite) by the bright green glow which it gave when exposed to the ultraviolet spark from an iron arc lamp. Research was undertaken to devise improved sources of ultraviolet radiation for the purpose of separating willemite conveniently by this property; thus today's phenomenal fluorescent lighting industry began. Every ton of the New Jersey Zinc Company's ore that went into the recent world-wide fighting was concentrated under ultraviolet light.

Some of the willemite continues to shine long after the ultraviolet rays are turned off. Such specimens are particularly beautiful when they are mixed with patches of white calcite which fluoresce a fine red color.

Not all willemite, however, fluoresces or phosphoresces. When it is pure, as in a few localities elsewhere in the world, this zinc silicate shows no evidence of either effect. Traces of manganese present in the New Jersey material give it the highly prized luminescence.

Fluorescent *diamonds* now appear to be much more abundant than they were formerly thought to be. Perhaps sixty-five per cent show this wonderful effect. The King of Gems may glow with varying intensity in almost any color. Sky blue or cornflower blue is the most typical of the stones from South Africa, though green and yellow are not uncommon. An occasional diamond phosphoresces and will be seen to glow in the dark after it has been exposed to sunlight; the most phosphorescent stones are those which fluoresce in daylight. Three hundred years ago the British scientist Robert Boyle experimented with diamonds that emitted light after being rubbed against fabric or wood; this type of luminescence is called *tribolu-minescence*. Boyle also noted that diamond fluoresces when heated; the property is called *thermoluminescence*.

Ruby, above all others, seems to deserve the distinction of being the chief luminescent gem. It does not react more strongly than some other stones, but it owes a large part of its glorious beauty to its rich scarlet fluorescence, which appears even in ordinary sunlight and serves to heighten the natural color of the gem and to make it superior to any other red stone. Rubies from Burma and Ceylon show more fluorescence than those from Siam.

If they are colored by chromium, *red spinel* and (to a lesser degree) *pink spinel* show a similar addition of fluo-rescence to their normal color. A similar effect of bright-ening can also be observed.

It is most appropriate to mention the fluorescence of *fluorite*, since that gem mineral gave its name to the phe-nomenon. Unfortunately for the nomenclature, a large proportion of fluorite is not visibly affected by ultraviolet radiation. The specimens that do respond usually show a blue-violet color, which is ascribed to the presence of rare-earth elements.

Kunzite, the lilac variety of spodumene, phosphoresces strongly in a fine pink hue.

Opal varies in its fluorescence, some specimens glowing only after they have been subjected to ultraviolet light for several minutes. Bluish and yellowish colors are common. The bright green of some opal is attributed to the presence

275

of radioactive substances, secondary uranium compounds. The yellowish-green fluorescence of *common opal* from Virgin Valley, Nevada, is very familiar to American collectors.

Examination of museum specimens of *jade* has showed that ageing may often be detected by the change in color of fluorescence, which declines from an intense purple in newly cut jade to white with blue and yellow mottling.

Amber fluoresces strongly, the color ranging from yellowish green to bluish white; the latter is most frequent.

Pearls fluoresce according to the waters from which the oysters were taken. The majority of those used in jewelry, from Ceylon, the Persian Gulf, and Australia, show a sky-blue color. The ethereal blue of Japanese *cultured pearls* is most appealing. An interesting difference between the fluorescence of cultured pearls and natural pearls is seen during their exposure to X-rays. Although the production of these rays for gem testing is generally not feasible, the standard apparatus for differentiating pearls, called an endoscope, uses X-rays. With them, cultured pearls are found to be by far the more fluorescent of the two types, especially when they have a mother-of-pearl bead as a nucleus.

To return to the corundum gems, other varieties besides ruby may be mentioned in connection with fluorescence. *Yellow corundum* fluoresces strongly in golden yellow. *Blue corundum* varies in intensity; stones from Montana and Ceylon glow more strongly than those from India.

Synthetic ruby fluoresces vividly, even more than the natural gem, owing to its greater content of chromium.

Certain colors of *synthetic spinel* display fluorescence in its choicest form. The yellowish-green stones, fluorescing in the same color, are particularly striking. The blue stones fluoresce brightly in red. The red fluorescence of

Fig. 112   Fluorescent Effects in Several Varieties of Quartz and Chalcedony

the recently developed American *synthetic emerald* serves as the easiest, though not the surest, means of distinguishing it from natural emerald, which usually does not fluoresce in ultraviolet light.

Other gems besides those discussed here (see Fig. 112) display occasional luminescent colors, which are so variable, depending so much upon the locality, that descriptions of them would resolve into a mere listing. The best way to become familiar with them is to see them in museums and to build a collection of them with which to experiment at home.

FLUORESCENT EQUIPMENT

The most important fact to be considered when equipment is being acquired for the production of fluorescent light is that, although the ultraviolet wavelengths cover only a tiny fraction of the electromagnetic series, they nevertheless extend over a wider range than is covered by any single source of illumination. More than one lamp is needed if all the fluorescent effects are to be obtained. A lamp designed for one part of the field will fail to illuminate the stones that respond only to a different part, for gems and minerals vary in their reaction to different radiation. In general, the available equipment is made for either "long" or "short" wavelengths, the latter being more desirable for most purposes. The ultraviolet range is about 1600 to 3800 angstrom units (A.U.), whereas the visible spectrum extends from 3800 to 8000 A.U., each of these units being one hundred-millionths of a centimeter in length.

A second essential fact to be remembered about fluorescent apparatus is that each of the lamps transmits a certain amount of visible light, which dilutes the fluorescence and confuses the effect. Consequently, a *filter* must usually be employed to eliminate as much of the daylight colors as possible. The proper filter depends, of course, upon the range of the lamp with which it is to be used. Care should be taken to protect one's eyes from the harmful effects of the invisible rays.

278

Besides a wide range of ultraviolet radiation, an ideal fluorescent lamp gives an intense and uniform illumination, free from unpleasant fumes or excessive heat, and capable of being enclosed for protection. An ideal filter transmits all the ultraviolet and none of the visible light. Some of the equipment made today approaches perfection in many ways.

Any discussion of ultraviolet sources should begin with the sun, for sunlight is rich in these rays. Much of the beauty of ruby is the result of its fluorescence in sunlight added to its natural color. Much fluorite, many diamonds, and some amber, opal, and kunzite are made lovelier in this manner.

Stokes used lightning in some of his studies of fluorescence, but this extreme method is scarcely recommended to the general public.

The cheapest and most convenient source of ultraviolet light is the *argon bulb*, shown in Fig. 113. It is similar in principle to the familiar neon sign except that it is filled with argon (mixed with other gases) and can be used like any electric light bulb on ordinary house current. Although quite weak, it is surprisingly effective with some gems. The glass prevents the transmission of short wavelengths, passing those from 3300 to 3700 A.U., the peak being at about 3600 A.U., but practically none of the energy is wasted in delivering heat; so little visible light is produced that no filter is needed.

Another source of ultraviolet light that does not require a filter is the *high-potential spark* between iron electrodes. The apparatus consists of a transformer, a condenser, and a pair of adjustable electrodes. Unlike the argon bulb,

279

this radiation is rich in the shorter wavelengths. It has a low intensity but is convenient for its range.

The true *iron arc* is a high-intensity, low-voltage arc between iron electrodes. It operates best on direct current and gives off a large amount of visible light which must be filtered out.

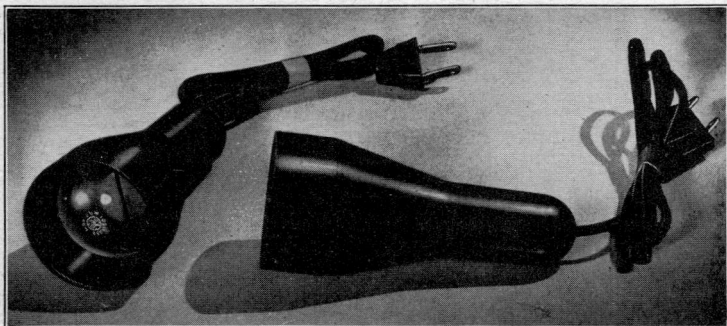

Fig. 113   Argon Bulb and Reflector for Producing Ultraviolet Light

[Ultra-Violet Products.]

The *carbon arc* gives large amounts of heat and visible light, but it combines the advantages of high intensity and wide range of wavelengths.

Of the various types of equipment the most suitable for the ultraviolet examination of most gems and minerals is some form of *mercury vapor lamp*, two kinds of which are shown in Figs. 114 and 115. The visible violet color of the incandescent gas is used in modern sign and street lighting. When a fused silica ("quartz") tube is used as the container, both high intensity and wide range, with the shorter wavelengths predominating, are obtained. An

Fig. 114   Lamp and Filter for Museum and Commercial Use

Fig. 115   Portable Model for Display or Field Use
Mercury Vapor Lamps for Creating Luminescence
[Ultra-Violet Products.]

excellent ultraviolet source when it is equipped with an appropriate filter is the *germicidal lamp* now widely used. A nickel-cobalt glass tube is convenient for museum installations, but it reduces the fluorescence as well as the amount of visible light. The same kind of glass is used in a bulb shape for the so-called *hot bulb*, which combines mercury vapor with a heating filament.

All this equipment, together with the newest improvements, is advertised regularly in popular mineral magazines. Manufacturers' catalogues supply detailed information about each article.

Index

283

Alexandrite, 108
  absorption spectrum in, 44
  crystallization of, 21
  synthetic, 252
  synthetic spinel resembling, 256
Alkali, caustic, effect of, on emerald, 13
Alkali feldspar, 178, 180
Allochromatic gem, 28
Alluvial deposits, *see* Placers
Alluvial diamond, 68, 87
Almandine, 145
Almandine spinel, 106
Almandite, 143, 144
  absorption spectrum in, 44
  in composite gems, 264
Almandite series, 143
Alps, gems from, 158, 195, 207, 212
Altered gems, 151
Aluminates, 12
Aluminum, abundance of, in gems, 12
Amateur lapidary, 202, 213
Amatrix, 172
Amazonite, 178
Amazonstone, 178
  crystallization of, 22, 176
Amber, 8, 233, 240
  composition of, 12
  effect of ether on, 14
  electricity in, 62
  fluorescence of, 276, 279
  from Baltic Sea, 68
  heat test for, 64
  imitation, 261
  insects in, 242, 243
  luster of, 31
  origin of, 69
  salt water test for, 53
  specific gravity of, 55

Amber, used for goiter, 3
Amber oil, 242
Amber pitch, 242
Amber varnish, 242
Ambergris, 244
Ambroid, 244
American cut, 73
American Gem Society, 4
American Museum of Natural History, 115, 136
Amethyst, 204
  cause of color in, 28
  crystallization of, 21
  resemblance to cordierite, 117
  treated, 266
Amethyst sapphire, 98
Amorphous gems, 16, 231
  absence of cleavage in, 60
  absence of dichroism in, 45
  effect of light on, 39, 40, 41
  fracture in, 60
  polarization in, 48
Amphibole group, 190
Amsterdam, diamond cutting in, 94
Amulets, gems used as, 1, 2
Andalusite, 158, 196
  crystallization of, 21
  polymorphism of, 15
Andes Mountains, Chile, lapis lazuli in, 183
Andesine, 179
Andradite, 143, 147
  dispersion in, 38
  luster of, 31
Andradite series, 143
Angola, diamond in, 88
Animal gems, 233
Animal products, distinguished from minerals, 6

284

Anodonta, 237
Anorthite, 179
Antero, Mount, Colorado, gems
    from, 135, 136, 140
Ant hills, olivine in, 139
Antigorite, 200
Antwerp, diamond cutting in, 94
Apatite, 115
    crystallization of, 21
    hardness of, 56
Apollo Belvedere, 205
Apostles, gems of the, 5
Aquamarine, 131, 134; *see also*
    Beryl
    chrysolite, 134
    crystallization of, 20
    resemblance to euclase, 154
    synthetic, 253
    synthetic spinel resembling, 256
    X-ray picture of, 24
Aqua regia, effect of, on gems,
    13
Arabia, pearl from, 237
Aragonite, in pearl, 234, 235
Arc, carbon, 280
    iron, 280
Argon bulb, 279, 280
Arizona, gems from, 139, 144,
    170, 173, 194,
    206, 223, 231
Arizona ruby, 102, 144
Arkansas, gems from, 90, 208
Arrows of love, 209
Artificial gems, 8, 247
Aru Islands, pearl from, 238
Asbestos, 191, 200, 210
Asia, *see names of countries*, Asia
    Minor, Banka, Middle East

Asia Minor, gems from, 172, 199,
    228, 245; *see also names of
    countries*
Asparagus-stone, 115
Assyria, lapis lazuli used in, 182
Asterism, 50, 102, 103, 250
Atlantic Ocean, coral from, 240
Atomic structure, *see* Structure,
    atomic
Atoms, 7, 16, 23, 24, 26, 55, 141
Australia, gems from, 57, 89, 104,
    112, 139, 146, 157, 159, 170,
    174, 193, 226, 227, 232, 237,
    240, 276; *see also* New
    South Wales, Queensland,
    South Australia, Tasmania
Austria, gems from, 119, 134, 154,
    162, 195
Aventurine, 206
Aventurine feldspar, 180
Axinite, 158
    crystallization of, 22
Axis, crystal, 17
Aztec jade carving, 187
Aztecs, obsidian used by, 230, 231
Azurite, 169, 170, 193
Azurmalachite, 171

Babylonia, lapis lazuli used in, 182
Baguette cut, 73
Bahia, Brazil, gems from, 89
Bakelite, 261
    salt water test for, 53
Balas ruby, 106
Ball, Sydney H., 65
Ballas, 97
Baltic Sea, amber from, 68, 240
Banded agate, 219
Band, absorption, 42
Banka, cassiterite from, 112
Bantam, 65
Barite, fluorescence of, 271

285

287

288

289

291

293

294

Heliotrope, 215
Hematite, 164, 166
  crystallization of, 21
  in aventurine, 206
  in sunstone, 180
  luster of, 31
  scientific, 262
  specific gravity of, 55
  streak of, 30
Hemimorphite, 167
Henderson, Edward P., 114

Henry II, 132
Henry V, 105
Herculaneum, emerald used in, 132
Herkimer diamond, 209
Herschel, Sir John, 271
Hessonite, 146
Hexagonal crystals, 18, 20
Hexagonal gems, effect of light on, 39, 40
Hexagonal system, 17, 20, 21
Hidden, William E., 121
Hiddenite, 121
  crystallization of, 21
High-potential spark, 279
High priest's breastplate, 5
High zircon, 148, 149
Hills of Precious Stones, Siam, ruby from, 101
Holmes, Ezekiel, 126
Honduras, carved jade from, 187
  white opal from, 226
Hope collection, 109
Hope diamond, 93, 94
Hot bulb, 282
Hungarian opal, 226
Hyacinth, 150, 151
Hyacinth-garnet, 146
Hyalite, 229

Hyderabad, Golconda, 89
Hydrocarbons, 12
Hydrochloric acid, effect of, on gems, 13
Hydrogen sulfide, effect of, on glass imitations, 12
Hydrophane, 229
Hypersthene, 118

Ice, crystallization of, 20
Iceland, obsidian from, 231
Iceland spar, 45
Identification, of composite gems, 264
  of gems, 18, 19
    by absorption spectrum, 42, 43
    by chemical tests, 25
    by color, 29
    by crystal form, 10
    by double refraction, 40, 48
    by hardness, 57
    by heat tests, 64
    by luster, 31
    by polarization, 48
    by refraction, 32
    by refractive index, 33, 34, 35
  of synthetic corundum, 253
  of synthetic emerald, 257
  optical instruments for, 43
Idiochromatic gem, 28
Idocrase, 194
  crystallization of, 19, 20
  jadelike, 200
Igmerald, 257
Igneous rocks, 66, 67
Illam, 152
Illinois, fluorite from, 113
Imitation emerald, flaws in, 132
Imitation gems, 8, 247, 259
Imitation opal, 114

296

298

Lapidary treatment of gems, 70, 71, 73, 74
Lapis, 183
Lapis lazuli, 8, 103, 167, 181, 182
  color in, importance of, 26
  effect of acid on, 13, 14
  imitated in jasper, 221
  origin of, 67
Lattice, 16
Lava, 65, 66
  gems in, 65, 66, 184, 229
Lazurite, 183
Leakage of light, 33
Lechosos opal, 226
Lens, hand, 27
Lepidolite, 130
Libyan Desert, silica-glass from, 231
Lichtenburg, diamond from, 87
Lifting of gems, 55
Light, absorption of, 26, 30
  bending of, 32
  composition of, 26
  diffraction of, in pearl, 236
  interference of, 50, 175, 180
    in opal, 224, 225
    in pearl, 236
  leakage of, 33
  speed of, 32
  ultraviolet, see Ultraviolet light
Lightning, fluorescence in, 279
Lightning Ridge opal field, New South Wales, 227
Lignite, 244
Limonite, 174
Linde Air Products Company, 250, 255
Little Namaqualand, diamond from, 87
Lombardy, Iron Cross of, 132

Loupe, jeweler's, 27
Low zircon, 148, 149, 150
Lozenge cut, 73
Luminescence, 51, 270
Luminescent gems, 270
Lure of gems, 1
Luster, 30, 55
  metallic, 164

Macedonians, pearl fishing by, 237
Madagascar, gems from, 116, 119, 120, 121, 122, 126, 127, 136, 137, 177, 178, 179, 180, 207, 208
Magazines, selected, 285
Magma, 66
Magnifier, utility, 27
Magnifying instruments, 27
Maine, gems from, 116, 122, 125, 136, 146, 181
  pearl essence from, 262
Malachite, 168, 171, 193
  banded, 169
  crystals of, 170
Manganese markings, 23
Mantle, 234, 235, 267
Manufactured chemicals, distinguished from minerals, 6
Maoris, nephrite used by, 192
Marble, 198
  dendrites on, 23
  marking in, 23
Marcasite, 166
Marco Polo, 107, 133, 183
Mark Antony, 224
Marker, diamond, 86
Marketing diamond, 87, 90
Marking diamond, 82
Marlborough collection, 109, 145
Marquise cut, 73

300

301

303

304

308

310

311

312